$\mathcal{A}$ GIFT FOR

⇥ FROM ⇤

500 Ways to
Throw Away
STRESS

500 Ways to Throw Away S T R E S S

Tips to Unclutter Your Life

Donna Smallin

BOK 5020

Edited by Robin Catalano
Interior illustrations by Carleen Powell
Text design by Susan Bernier
Text production by Jennifer Jepson Smith
Indexed by Susan Olason, Indexes & Knowledge Maps

Special edition published in 2000 for Hallmark Cards, Inc., by
Storey Books, Schoolhouse Road, Pownal, Vermont 05261

Contents

Dedication

For Gramma with love

Acknowledgments

I would like to thank Camaron J. Thomas (who thanks her teachers) for introducing me to Ayurveda and generously sharing a wealth of knowledge about coping with stress. *Namaste.*

Introduction

S tressed out? Who isn't! Experts estimate that nearly 10 million Americans seek psychiatric help each year for stress-related issues. And a whopping 80 percent of health care is spent on stress-related disorders.

When I told an acquaintance that I was writing a book about ways to throw away stress, she asked, "Is it possible to be completely stress-free?" The answer is absolutely, positively . . . no.

It's impossible to avoid stress. Instead, our goal is to learn how to cope with it. For the most part, that means learning to cope with change. You see, it's change that causes stress by forcing us to make adjustments in our lives. Even positive changes, such as a promotion at work or a complete recovery from breast cancer, can cause stress.

Unfortunately, the rapidly changing world in which we live tends to keep us in a constant state of emergency or *dis*tress. This is a problem because too much stress over a prolonged period of time can lead to emotional burnout or physical or psychological breakdown.

But don't despair. There's a lot you can do to cope with change and, in doing so, "throw away" stress. I hope that the tips in this book will help you to create a happier, more peaceful, and satisfying life.

Chapter 1

Empower Yourself

In this chapter...
- *Regain Control*
- *Learn to Relax*
- *Live Authentically*
- *Follow Your Bliss*

Regain Control

You've probably heard the saying that change is the only constant in life. Well, guess what? Change is the chief cause of stress — not just negative changes, but also positive changes and even perceived changes. One surefire way to reduce stress is to regain control over those things that are within your power.

Identify Stressors

Define your stressors. Where are you, whom are you with, and what are you most likely to be doing when you feel most stressed?

Admit whatever role you play in the stress you feel. Choose to react differently.

Keep a journal. Writing can help you get in touch with your true feelings, which can lead to important insights and discoveries about the cause and effect of stress in your life — and what you can do about it.

Disarm stress. Neutralize the effect of stressors by learning to replace your automatic stress response with a relaxation response. Take a few deep breaths. Count to 10. Take a five-minute walk. Or laugh out loud.

Quick Stress Relief

When you're in the middle of a crisis, remind yourself that this, too, shall pass.

Postpone changes when your stress level is high. Don't start any new projects or commitments. Don't change your living environment. Don't even change your hairstyle!

Exchange one stress for another. If you are experiencing a major change (positive or negative) in one area of your life, allow yourself some slack in another area. For instance, if you just started a new job, you might spend a little less time cleaning house to make a little more time for restful activities.

Take some time off. You might think that you can't afford to take time off from your responsibilities at home, work, or school, but if you're overstressed, you can't afford not to.

Don't just drift along. If you are in a troublesome or stressful situation, don't try to avoid the problem. Take action by taking a chance. Taking chances is the key to emotional well-being.

Don't let one aspect of your life dominate your life. Try to balance work and play, family and social life, physical and spiritual activities.

Turn your world upside down. Instead of dwelling on what you wish you had, be thankful for what you have right now.

Reach out for help. If you are having difficulty functioning because of stress, don't be afraid to consult with your health care provider.

> *The first step in becoming a more peaceful person is to have the humility to admit that, in most cases, you are creating your own emergencies. Life will usually go on even if things don't go according to plan. It's helpful to remember that life isn't an emergency.*
>
> — Richard Carlson, Ph.D.

Accept all offers of help. Let someone else prepare dinner. Take up your friend's kind offer to babysit. Pay the neighborhood kids to shovel your driveway or mow your lawn.

Long-Term Strategies

Practice the concept of "pace, not race." Walk and talk more slowly. Give yourself more time to meet deadlines and complete your work. Allow yourself time to relax each day.

Practice acceptance. We often get distressed about things that we won't let ourselves accept, such as someone else's feelings, beliefs, or actions. Ask yourself, "Is this within my power to change?" If not, let it go.

Spend more time with people who help you feel better about yourself.

Always give your best. Whether you are trying to lose weight, launch a new career, or save a faltering marriage, try your best. If it doesn't work out, you can be secure in the knowledge that you did everything within your power. Remember that nothing worth doing is easy.

Put yourself first. It's not being selfish; it's being self-caring. Caring for yourself — physically, emotionally, intellectually, socially, and spiritually — will make you happier, healthier, and better able to cope with the demands of daily living. In fact, by reserving even just a little more time and energy for yourself, you will feel less stress and have more to give to others.

Overcome the stress of procrastination. Delaying or avoiding more important tasks is a surefire recipe for producing high-stress situations. If you're a perfectionist, try to think in terms of excellence versus perfection. In many cases, "good enough" truly is good enough and "perfect" isn't worth the extra time and effort.

Get organized. Use a daily "things to do" list. Straighten up your work and living areas. Streamline your schedule. Exercise in the morning so you only need to shower once. If you have errands to run, group them together by geographic location so that you minimize driving time.

Think of life as your party. As the host, you might get unwelcome "guests" from time to time. It's your job to escort them to the door. Call for help if you have to! Just remember that it's your house and it's up to you to decide who (or what) stays and who (or what) goes.

Learn from your dog. Speak up if you want something. Accept love and attention. Don't hold your mistakes against yourself. Get outside and play every day.

Reduce the disappointment factor. Be realistic about your expectations. Allow yourself to "roll with the punches." Be a graceful loser. Look for the lesson in your disappointment and use what you have learned to get greater satisfaction from your life.

Learn to Relax

If your life is a whirlwind of activity seven days a week, try balancing it with some true leisure time — time to just sit — without feeling the need to be productive or occupied. Taking time for you will refresh your spirit and make you more efficient when you return to your responsibilities.

Let your spirit soar. Making time for pursuits that elevate your soul will help you maintain balance and perspective in your life and give you better control over stress.

Throughout the day, take mini-breaks. Sit down and practice some deep breathing, or stretch to release tension in your muscles. Smile, and say something positive, such as "I am relaxed."

Take it easy. If you work particularly long and hard one day or if you feel exhausted, make a conscious effort to take it a little easier the next day.

Breathe to the power of 10. When you find yourself clenching your teeth or tightening up your muscles in response to a stressor, take a deep breath to the count of 10 and exhale to the count of 10. Repeat several times.

Change up. A change from your regular routine can be just as relaxing as a rest. Try doing something you really love to do but haven't done in a long while.

Take a day off. If you've been swamped with deadlines, spend a whole day with no plans. Just do what you feel like doing, when you feel like doing it.

PROGRESSIVE RELAXATION EXERCISE

To give yourself a time-out, try this relaxing and refreshing exercise.

Put on some relaxing music and then set a timer for 20 minutes or so. Lie flat on your back on a carpeted floor or mat. Take a deep breath in, and slowly let it out. Continue to breathe deeply. Follow each breath with your mind; really focus on each inhalation and exhalation. Let yourself relax into each breath. Relax your feet. Imagine that they are growing very heavy and that the feeling of heaviness is spreading very slowly through your body, from your toes, up through your legs, to your hips and lower back, chest and shoulders, and arms and hands. Even your face feels heavy, as if gravity is pulling it down into the floor. Just lie there, enjoying the stillness of the moment. When the timer goes off, slowly deepen your breaths and begin to stretch. Roll to one side for a minute, and then sit up slowly.

Live Authentically

Living authentically is about making your actions consistent with your values. When you make a choice to live your life according to your values, you will find more time, less stress, and a sense of personal freedom.

Why should the lord of the country
Flit about like a fool?
If you let yourself be blown to and fro,
You lose touch with your root.
If you let restlessness move you,
You lose touch with who you are.

— Lao-Tzu

Identify What's Important

Look inside. Take a personal retreat in which you devote a few hours or even a whole day or two — perhaps with a few friends — to talk about your sense of purpose in life and how you want to spend your time here on earth. Stopping and thinking can change your life.

Make a list of your values. These are the qualities you admire and respect in yourself and others. Honesty, resourcefulness, intelligence, style, and simplicity are just a few examples. Identify your values by looking at the "whys" behind how you spend your time and money. Are you living consistently with your values?

Imagine that you have only a short time to live. In *Live Your Dream,* Joyce Chapman suggests this exercise: Think back over the past month. How would you spend your time differently? How would your priorities change? What would become more (or less) important to you?

WHO ARE YOU REALLY?

In *Live Your Dream*, Joyce Chapman encourages us to pay conscious attention to what we are thinking and doing as a tool for questioning and ultimately understanding who we really are "beneath all the shoulds, buts, and external influences." Chapman suggests that you notice:

- Your first thought when waking up
- As you prepare for the day, whether you are excited or filled with dread
- Whether you look for the good or focus on the problem
- The most important part and the most enjoyable part of your day
- What it is that you willingly set aside everything else to do
- The kind of people you hang out with and how you feel around them (alive or bored, for example)
- Whom you're attracted to and why
- Whom you try to impress
- How you feel when someone asks you what work you do
- Moments when you feel fully alive
- What you keep putting off
- What you appreciate
- What you remembered, and what you forgot
- Whom you put first and last

Become aware of what you believe. Positive beliefs drive positive behaviors; negative beliefs drive negative behaviors. For example, if you want to lose weight because your clothes are getting uncomfortable but you don't change your eating or exercise habits, perhaps you believe that you don't deserve to feel good. To change your behavior, you've got to change that belief.

A human being
Fashions his consequences
As surely as he fashions
His goods or his dwelling.
Nothing he says,
Thinks or does
Is without consequences.

— Norman Cousins

Rededicate Your Life

Enjoy simple pleasures. Look around instead of racing around. Try to find one thing each day that you never noticed before.

Reclaim the power of choice. When you let someone else make choices for you, you are giving up the power to make yourself happy. Reclaim that power and all the happiness that is rightfully yours.

Make time for fun. Plan time to enjoy your favorite amusements as often as possible. You'll feel better before, during, and after.

Do unto others. You can get in the habit of feeling good by being good to yourself and others.

Just *don't* do it. Stopping *is* an option. If the reason you continue to do something is because you've been doing it for a while and feel it would be time and energy wasted to stop now, think again. Think about all the things you could be doing but can't do because you don't have the time. If you are unhappy, unfulfilled, or unsatisfied, give yourself permission to leave this thing behind and move on.

Give it a try. Be willing to try something new to see how it works. If you keep doing things the same way, you'll keep getting the same results.

To change your life, follow the simple yet valuable advice of Dr. William James, the founder of modern psychology:
- Start immediately.
- Do it flamboyantly.
- Make no exceptions.

Be Your Best Self

Once you've determined your beliefs and values, you are ready to put them into action. Don't be afraid to let the world see who you really are. When you "be yourself," you give others permission to do the same. With no false fronts to keep up, life is simpler, less stressful, and more satisfying.

Develop a vision statement. A vision statement is a proclamation about what you want to be and what you want to achieve or contribute. Take some time to write it down. Keep it where you will see it frequently. Read it aloud.

Make a list of things that make you happy. Challenge yourself to come up with at least 100 ideas. Then resolve to do at least three of those things each day for the next three weeks.

Develop affirmations. An affirmation is a positive statement that often begins with the words "I will" or "I can" or "I am." An example of an affirmation for a cancer patient is: "I can feel myself growing healthier and stronger each day." Write several affirmations and post them somewhere as a reminder to say them aloud every day. The power of affirmations does not come from writing or reading them but from the vibrations of saying them aloud.

Live with no regrets. If you were to die tomorrow, what would you regret not having done? How can you live your life today, and every day, so that you will have no regrets?

Be gentle with yourself. If you find yourself slipping back into old patterns, congratulate yourself for recognizing that! Then reclaim your will and move on.

Finding Your Balance

Imagine life as a game in which you are juggling five balls. Name them: work, family, health, friends, spirit. Work is a rubber ball; if you drop it, it will bounce back. But the other four balls — family, health, friends, and spirit — are made of glass. If you drop one of these, it might be irrevocably damaged.

Focus on one thing at a time. When you are with your family, give them 100 percent of your attention. When you are at work, engage fully in your job. And when you are playing, have fun!

Be flexible with your schedule. Don't try to plan every minute of your time. Leave time to do whatever you feel like doing at the moment, which may be nothing at all.

Delegate. Too much "home" work and not enough fun? List daily and weekly jobs at home. Give some of your jobs to family members who are able to help.

Schedule time for fun. At the beginning of each month, put "fun stuff to do" on your calendar to balance the demands and responsibilities of home and career. Include family events as well as things that will give you private time.

Follow Your Bliss

What do you love to do? What makes you happy to be alive? If your time and money were not objects, what would you do? Recognizing the things that give you joy and satisfaction — and increasing the amount of time you spend doing them — puts you on the path to increased happiness and fulfillment.

Step back and see yourself through another set of eyes. Pretend that you are someone who has just met you. What desirable qualities might this person you've just created see in you?

Don't confuse skills with talents. Look not at what you *can* do, but at what you *want* to do. For example, you may have learned how to do your current job very well, but that doesn't mean it's what you want to do. If you do a job because that's what you know how to do and not because you want to do it, you are likely to be very unhappy.

Close your eyes and visualize yourself working at your dream job. In what type of environment are you working? What kind of people are you working with, and what sort of interaction do you have with them? The more vivid you can make your vision, the more it will help to clarify your dream.

Do what you are. "By unlocking the secrets of your personality type, you *can* find a truly fulfilling job that enhances the quality of your life," say Paul D. Tieger and Barbara Barron-Tieger, authors of the book *Do What You Are*. Based on a scientific approach to categorizing personalities in 16 distinct types, the book is a wonderful resource for helping you match your personality with a satisfying and rewarding career.

WHAT ARE YOUR S.W.O.T.s?

Businesspeople often analyze the viability of ideas and develop strategies based on the S.W.O.T. technique. Try it as a tool for assessing your own goals.

- **Strengths.** What strengths do you possess that will enable you to succeed? List your talents and skills.
- **Weaknesses.** Identify your weaknesses. What can you do to shore up these weaknesses? Develop and implement a plan of action.
- **Opportunities.** What is going on in the world around you? Can you see any trends? Where is the greatest need for your expertise or talent?
- **Threats.** What obstacles stand in your way? How big a threat are these obstacles to your success? What can you do to minimize or steer around these obstacles?

Don't Just Dream It, Live It!

Make a dream board. One idea from the book *Live Your Dream* is to cut out magazine pictures and words, use photos, or draw illustrations that portray your dream of who you want to be. Include the aspects of life such as family, friends, and accomplishments that are important to you. Put this dream board in a place where you will see it every day.

Think back to your childhood. What did you want to be when you grew up? What kind of response did you get from your parents or teachers? Often, we don't follow our original passion because of negative feedback we received at a tender age. For example, you might have wanted to be an astronaut, but your parents told you that you didn't do well enough in science or math. Don't ever let others stop you from pursuing your dreams.

Go for It

How do you know whether what you want is what will make you happy? There is only one way to know for sure: Go for it. Allowing yourself to follow your true passion will not only enhance your life, it will also give you the sense of accomplishment that comes from taking action.

Never say no to yourself. Callie Khouri, the screenwriter of *Thelma & Louise,* had always wanted to write but lacked the confidence to try. One night, while sitting in her car, the idea for *Thelma & Louise* hit her like a brick. Although she had never attended film school, she decided not to give in to her usual self-doubt because along with the movie idea came a feeling of release: "I am not going to say no to myself anymore." The movie became a box-office smash, and today Callie Khouri is a full-time professional screenwriter.

Break goals into mini goals. In *Life Mapping,* author Bill Cohen suggests dividing your goals into a list of activities necessary to complete those goals. Keep breaking the items on the list into smaller and smaller activities, until each individual activity can be completed within a week or a day. Take this list and put it in chronological order (what you need to do this week, next week, and so on). Then get going.

Don't be afraid to fail. Were you able to swim or ride a bike on your first try? Probably not. In failing, we learn what doesn't work, which frees us to try other approaches that might work — until we finally succeed. The only real failure is not trying at all.

Be brave. What's the worst possible thing that could happen? This is an excellent question to ask yourself when you are faced with a difficult decision or you are afraid to do something.

> *Whatever you can do or dream you can, begin it. Boldness has beauty, power and magic in it.*
>
> — Johann Wolfgang von Goethe

Chapter 2

Destress Your Body

In this chapter . . .

- *Sweat Away Stress*
- *Daily Relaxation*
- *Nutrition and Stress*
- *Maintain a Healthy Weight*
- *Mmmm . . . Massage*
- *Staying Well*

L et's face it: Stress isn't just in your mind. You feel it in your body, too. In small doses, stress can help you stay alert and focused, but too much stress can damage your body and mind.

When you are under stress, how does *your* body respond? Many people complain of such physical symptoms as tension in the neck or shoulders, headaches, backaches, upset stomach, fitful sleep, or fatigue. But stress also lowers the immune system response, increasing the chances of frequent colds and flus. More important, prolonged stress can lead to high blood pressure, heart attacks, heart disease, certain types of asthma, many forms of cancer, alcoholism, and depression.

So what can you do to destress your body? Listen to it. Respond to its distress signals. Make it healthier and stronger, because when your body is at its best, you look and feel your best.

Sweat Away Stress

Aerobic exercise is great for your health, and it's one of the ultimate stress-beaters. It not only eases mild depression and anxiety but also helps regulate stress-related hormones and makes you feel better about your body, which makes you feel better about yourself.

Where Do I Begin?

Start slow and easy. If you are just starting an exercise program, especially if you're over 40, begin with 10 to 15 minutes a day at a pace that's comfortable for you. Over a period of a few weeks, gradually increase the length of your workout to 30 minutes or more each day.

Choose whatever physical activity feels right for you. If you're a fighter by nature, you might choose to let off steam through sports that involve hitting or kicking a ball. If your instinct is to take flight at the first sign of stress, try walking or running. If you are naturally quiet or introspective, you might find that vigorous yoga practice is the perfect solution.

Try to get a minimum of 30 minutes of moderate physical activity at least five days a week. (*Hint*: Aim for every day. Then, even if you miss a day or two, you'll still meet your goal.)

Sticking with It

Exercise at the same time each day. Block off the time in your day planner, and keep the appointment as you would any other appointment. That way, you won't have to "stress" over when you'll fit it into each day.

Mark an X on your calendar each day that you exercise. Seeing all those Xs will help keep you motivated.

No time? You don't have to do all 30 minutes at once. Three 10-minute workouts throughout the day will provide the same stress-relieving benefits. Here are some ways to fit exercise into your day:

- Get off your commuter bus or train one stop early and walk to work.
- Park on the perimeter of the parking lot and walk to the building.
- Use part of your lunch hour to walk.
- Climb stairs instead of using the elevator or escalator.
- Put on music and dance while you're cleaning the house.
- Play active games with your kids.

Rediscover the joy of playing! If the word "workout" keeps you from exercising, think of it as playtime. Try doing some of the things you used to do as a kid. Go for a bike ride. Walk with a friend. Swim at the community center pool. Or take dancing lessons with your partner.

Daily Relaxation

Effective stress management begins with regaining some control over the pace of your life. And that means making a conscious effort to build relaxation time into every day. You will discover that as little as 5 to 15 minutes of self-care each day can make a dramatic difference in your stress level.

Sighs of Relief

Deep breathing techniques are very effective for reducing physical and mental stress. That's because focusing on your breath will help to slow you down.

Practice taking complete breaths. Watch a baby breathe and you can see her belly expand as she inhales and contract as she exhales. This is how we're meant to breathe, but as we get older we tend to breathe more shallowly. Taking complete breaths is something you can practice every day — upon awakening, before going to sleep, and during times of stress to help relax your body.

Physiologically, stretching increases blood flow, which makes tight muscles more relaxed. Stretching for a few minutes as much as once every hour prevents tension from building up in your body. You can even perform specific stretches for your arms, legs, back, shoulders, and neck. Or simply stretch as you would if you were just waking up. Taking several minutes to breathe and stretch your muscles will make you feel calmer and more focused.

Try So-Hum breathing. As you inhale, silently say the word "So." As you exhale, silently say the word, "Hum." So-Hum breathing is often used to focus the mind before beginning a meditation practice.

Get into deep breathing. Constrict the back of your throat. Inhale and exhale slowly while saying the word "ha" through your closed mouth. It should sound as if you are breathing through a heavy mask. In yoga, this type of breathing is known as *ujjayi* ("sound of the ocean") breathing.

Nutrition and Stress

Balanced nutrition provides your body with energy stores to draw upon during stressful times. Eating well also makes you feel more in control and better about yourself. Some foods, such as whole grains, rice, raisins, room-temperature fruit, cooked vegetables, and warming spices like ginger and cinnamon, can increase calmness. Other foods, such as potato chips, doughnuts, chocolate, and coffee, can cause physical distress because they produce short rushes of energy followed by a slump.

Develop Good Eating Habits

When you're always on the go, it's not easy to eat right. Yet, proper nutrition is a simple, effective way to avoid putting undue stress on your body. Insufficient intake of nutrients translates into an inability for your body to function at its best. Following are some simple guidelines for developing good eating habits:

- Eat foods in their natural state as often as possible; for example, raw fruits and vegetables, beans, nuts, and seeds.
- Choose whole grains (whole wheat, oat bran) over more refined and processed grains in pasta, breads, and cereals.
- Eat two fruits or vegetables at each meal.
- Eat no more than two servings daily of fish, chicken, turkey, lean beef, or pork. A serving is only about 3 ounces, or the size of a deck of cards.
- Eat a variety of foods.
- Choose skim or 1 percent milk over whole milk and nonfat or low-fat cheeses over regular cheeses.
- Incorporate soy products into your diet.

- Go light on butter, margarine, oils, sugar, salt, and alcohol.
- Cut back on processed foods.
- Drink at least eight 8-ounce glasses of water each day — more on days you exercise.

Don't eat too much. Eat three meals a day, but stick with one regular-size helping at each meal. Eating a light snack — such as a handful of pumpkin seeds, a few pretzels, or some carrot sticks with hummus — *between* meals may help to prevent you from overeating *at* meals.

Don't eat too little. Calories equal energy, which you need for "fight or flight." Even if you're trying to lose weight, you should still eat three balanced meals a day.

Don't skip breakfast. Eating a healthy breakfast provides fuel for your mind and body. Here are some ideas for energy-boosting breakfasts:

- Nonfat or low-fat yogurt and an English muffin spread lightly with jam
- Cereal with skim or 1 percent milk and sliced fruit, plus a slice of whole wheat toast spread very lightly with peanut butter
- A toasted English muffin topped with one slice of lean ham or turkey and/or low-fat cheese and then broiled, plus a piece of fruit
- Hot oatmeal with raisins and skim milk

- Scrambled eggs (one or two) sprinkled with shredded low-fat cheese and rolled up in a whole wheat tortilla with salsa on top

Vitamin and Herbal Support

There are a number of herbal supplements that may help to combat the symptoms of stress. Be sure to talk to your doctor about which herbs and vitamins might be right for you.

Soothe your spirit and muscles with kava kava. This herb is believed to promote a state of contentment and a greater sense of well-being as well as physical and mental relaxation and increased concentration.

If you're suffering from stress-induced depression, St.-John's-wort may offer welcome relief. But do not self-treat! Consult your doctor or psychiatrist for advice.

THE AYURVEDIC APPROACH

Ayurveda, which means "science of life" in Sanskrit, is an ancient healing system. It is based on the belief that each person's internal and external makeup falls into one of three broad categories of body types.

Vata body types are aggravated by irregular hours, too much aerobic exercise, and too many activities. They experience increased hyperactivity and anxiety in times of stress. Solutions include a routine for waking and sleeping; eating warm, cooked foods that are not dry or too light; and warming scents. Walking is the preferred exercise.

Pitta body types are aggravated by hot and spicy food, overactive people, and heat-inducing activities and react to stress with anger and irritability. Pittas need cooling food and cooling activities, such as walking or swimming (competitive sports are not desirable). These body types benefit greatly from learning new ways to respond in challenging situations.

Kaphas are aggravated by too little activity and boredom; their reaction to stress is apathy. They respond well to light, dry foods; exercise of some sort every day; and stretching.

For more information about the practice of Ayurveda or to find an Ayurvedic physician in your area, consult your local Yellow Pages or call the American Ayurvedic Association at (877) 598-8830.

Try the great peacemaker. Licorice root, also known as "the great peacemaker," is another herb believed to have pacifying effects. A rich source of antioxidants, licorice supports the adrenal glands, which help your body to resist stress.

Mind your Bs. B-complex vitamins are vital for healthy nervous system function, and chronic stress increases the demand for these nutrients. If you are not eating at least six servings of whole-grain breads and cereals daily, you may benefit from a B-complex vitamin supplement.

Maintain a Healthy Weight

One of the best ways to avoid physical stress is to maintain a healthy weight, which for many of us means shedding a few pounds. And there's only one way to do it: For every pound you want to lose, you've got to "lose" 3,600 calories. You do that by either consuming 3,600 fewer calories or burning them off through exercise. It's simple — in theory anyway.

In practice, maintaining a healthy weight can be an endless battle. But it's a battle that's well worth the fight; not only will you look and feel better, but also you'll reduce your risk of heart disease, diabetes, cancer, and a variety of other medical problems that can create more stress in your life.

Take It Off

If you are more than 10 percent over your healthy weight, aim for one to two pounds of weight loss per week. Remember: To lose weight, you need to consume fewer calories, burn more, or both. If you walk at a moderate pace for 30 minutes every day, eat sensibly, and cut out a couple of desserts a week, you could lose about one pound in a week.

Avoid fad diets, especially diets that severely restrict caloric intake or entire groups of foods. You may lose weight quickly following one fad or another, but quick weight loss is usually followed by quick weight gain — and more stress.

Be patient. Allow yourself time to achieve your healthy weight. Once you get going, weight loss adds up fast.

Make small changes. If you simply replace one 8-ounce glass of regular soda a day (100 calories) with water, you can lose 10 pounds in a year — painlessly.

Control Is the Key

Live for today. In *Get Real: A Personal Guide to Real-Life Weight Management,* author Daniel Kosich, Ph.D., suggests that you focus on taking care of yourself today, not achieving some future weight goal. He also recommends applying the 80/20 rule to what you eat: Eat what you know you should 80 percent of the time and leave 20 percent for acknowledging and accepting that you're not perfect.

Remember that all foods are okay to eat — just not okay to eat at all times. So when you are tempted to eat a slice of gooey chocolate cake or a bag of greasy potato chips, try saying to yourself, "I'm not going to eat this today because right now I'm trying to eat healthier foods. I can have that some other time." Recognizing that these foods are not forbidden forever makes it easier to turn them down.

Eat more earlier in the day and less later. If you can, make breakfast your biggest meal, followed by a substantial lunch and a very light supper.

Get a handle on portions. If you think you're eating the right stuff but still can't shake excess weight, reduce your portions. Americans tend to underestimate what they eat by 50 percent. For example, the bagel you eat for breakfast is most likely not one, but two or even three servings of grains. The official USDA serving size for a bagel is 2 ounces — a far cry from the 4 to 6 ounces of the average bagel.

Dine out less often. It's easy to be tempted into eating high-fat, high-calorie foods when you order off a menu. Eating at home lets you maintain more control of what goes in your mouth (and onto your hips, thighs, or waist!).

If you're restricting calories, watch what you drink. A glass of juice is a healthier choice than a glass of soda, but it has about the same amount of calories. Water is always the best choice.

Read labels. You don't have to read everything on the label, but do look at serving size, fat, and calories. A 1999 survey by the American Dietetic Association shows that consumers who read food labels get 30 percent of their calories from fat; nonreaders get 35 percent. Look for products that have a big difference between the total calories and the number of fat calories.

Cook lighter. Many recipes call for more sugar, salt, or fat than is really necessary. Replace the oil, butter, or fat in baked goods with half as much applesauce. You can also try fruit-based fat replacers, which are sold in most supermarkets.

Eat less for dinner. Decrease your appetite by eating a healthy mid-afternoon snack. Exercise for 30 to 60 minutes just prior to your evening meal. Drink a large glass of water before sitting down to eat, or eat a salad before your main course.

Reshape Your Attitude

Enjoy yourself. Don't let being self-conscious about your body get in the way of participating in activities you enjoy. You have the right to enjoy any activities regardless of your body shape or size.

Thinner isn't always better. If you eat right and exercise but can't seem to reach your ideal body weight, don't stress out about it. First, consult with your physician to make sure there aren't any underlying problems. If everything checks out okay, relax. It's probably that your "ideal" is based on the media's idealistic — and often unrealistic — body image.

Put success into perspective. Do honor your goal to be fit and healthy, but don't fret if you never lose that last 10 pounds or develop "killer abs."

You are still a beautiful person with the potential to achieve a happy, healthy, successful life.

Mmmm . . . Massage

Massage triggers relaxation responses in your body by stimulating the release of endorphins, the body's natural painkillers, and by acting as a sedative to the nervous system. It's a soothing, relaxing therapy that can reduce mental and physical tension, lower blood pressure, increase flexibility, improve posture. and promote better circulation.

Incorporate regular massage into your wellness practice. It may seem extravagant at first, but you can't put a price on your physical and mental well-being. Self-massage is also an alternative.

Do It Yourself

Massage your shoulders. Use your right hand to work on your left shoulder and left hand to work on your right shoulder. Work your fingers gently but firmly, beginning with your shoulder blade, moving up toward the neck. Don't forget to include the scalp.

Try acupressure. When you fold your third finger over on your palm, it points to a pressure point that you can massage with the thumb of your other hand. Many people find that massaging this spot is very relaxing.

Tennis anyone? Press the sole of your foot on a tennis ball, moving it around to fully massage your entire foot. Press hard on the ball as if you are trying to flatten it. Use a relatively new tennis ball for maximum effect.

Enjoy a soothing, après shower massage. Put a few drops of oil on one palm and then rub both palms briskly together. Apply the oil all over your body after showering.

Incorporate mini pampering sessions into your regular routine. For example, when you apply hand cream, don't just rub it in; massage your palms, the tops of your hands, and along the length of each finger.

Trade nightly foot massages or backrubs with your partner.

Staying Well

Implementing healthful habits will go a long way toward alleviating chronic stress and the symptoms that come with it. And being healthy makes you feel good about yourself, which makes you feel better about everything and everyone around you. You may find that the things that used to stress you out don't seem so stressful.

Healthful Habits

Treat your body with respect. Give it enough rest. Fuel it with a variety of foods. Exercise it appropriately, and listen to what it needs.

Get eight hours of sleep each night. Research suggests that sleep deprivation boosts levels of stress-related hormones, like adrenaline, which in turn increases the risk of hypertension, stroke, and other cardiovascular problems. Lack of sleep is one of the chief causes of daytime fatigue, which can lead to traffic accidents and on-the-job injuries. Sleep deficiency is also associated with lowered immunity to illness and disease. The following are some tips for getting a better night's sleep:

- Go to bed at the same time each night and get up at the same time each morning.
- Avoid stimulants like tea, coffee, cola, and cocoa before going to bed.

- Eat dinner three to four hours before going to bed to allow time for your body to digest.
- Exercise every day, but do it earlier in the day rather than later.
- Use your bedroom primarily for sleeping — not for activities like eating, reading, or watching television.
- Avoid or limit daytime naps.
- Listen to relaxation tapes to fall asleep.
- If you can't get to sleep within 15 minutes, get up and read or watch television until you feel sleepy.

Avoid distress habits — smoking cigarettes, overeating, using drugs, drinking too much alcohol. You need to be physically and mentally alert to deal effectively with stress. If just the thought of quitting produces stress, or if you or someone close to you thinks you may have a problem, please seek help.

Drink to your health. Sufficient water consumption helps all of your vital organs (including your brain) function better. Lack of fluid intake can result in fatigue, weakness, listlessness, sore muscles, jitters, and even the blues. A good rule is to drink twice as much water as it takes to quench your thirst. If you hate the taste of plain water, add a squeeze (or a few slices) of fresh lemon, lime, or orange, or try mixing in a splash of cranberry juice.

Celebrate wellness! Let your birthday be a reminder each year to schedule an annual physical exam. Regular checkups can help to catch potential health problems before they become serious. Taking better care of yourself now will help you live longer with fewer disabilities and health problems.

See your dental hygienist twice a year. Don't have dental insurance? Have your teeth cleaned twice a year anyway. Regular cleanings will prevent the buildup of plaque and tartar that can lead to tooth decay and more serious problems. The $60 to $70 you pay for each visit can save you hundreds and thousands of dollars in the long run.

Floss! According to the January 1999 *Journal of Periodontology*, nearly one-third of all Americans between the ages of 30 and 54 have periodontitis, an advanced stage of bone loss that has been linked to diabetes, respiratory disease, and heart attacks. That's stress you can do without. The best prevention? Brush and floss your teeth daily.

Wash your hands frequently. Soap and water are the best prevention against germs that can cause colds. Forget the antibacterial soap; any soap will do. For best results, wash your hands like nurses do: for a full 60 seconds. (To keep the tops of your hands from drying out, wash only the palms. Follow up with moisturizer.)

Chapter 3

Unwind
Your Mind

In this chapter . . .

- *Don't Worry — Be Present*
- *Cultivating Mindfulness*
- *Daily Stress Busters*
- *Enjoy Yourself!*
- *Soothing Rituals*

I n chapter 1, you learned how to get a grip on stress rather than letting it get a grip on you. In chapter 2, you learned how you can relieve physical stress while also creating a stronger, healthier body. In this chapter, you will learn to unwind your mind to achieve a calmer, more peaceful state.

> *Yesterday is history, tomorrow is a mystery, and today is a gift. That's why it is called the present.*
>
> — Anonymous

Don't Worry — Be Present

When you're traveling at warp speed as so many of us do (on autopilot, no less), you tend not to think much about what you're doing in and with your life. In the "busyness" of living, we lose ourselves as well as the precious moments of time. But our time on earth is the only time we have!

Most of our worries are about things that never actually happen or things that have already happened. There's a famous old southern expression: Don't worry that the mule is blind — just load the wagon.

Repeat to yourself as often as needed each day: Where am I? Here. What time is it? Now.

Don't let setbacks rule your life. What's done is done. Move on.

Cultivating Mindfulness

Despite the seeming simplicity, it's not easy to "stop and smell the roses." The fact is that we've trained ourselves to be constantly on the go, to always be doing *something* and thinking ahead. But if you never live in and fully enjoy the present, what kind of life are you living? How much are you missing out on?

Practice Awareness

Slow down. Try this simple exercise: Stand up and deliberately move across the room in slow motion. Notice how it increases your awareness and expands time. That's what slowing down in life can do for you.

Don't just do something, sit there. Take time now to look at what's going on around you. What do you see and hear? What do you feel? Stopping every once in a while makes you more aware of what you are doing when you start moving again.

> *It's only possible to live happily ever after on a moment-to-moment basis.*
>
> — Margaret Bonnano

EATING MINDFULLY

Make it a point to sit down when you eat. When eating, be mindful (or aware) of each mouthful of food. Notice the texture as well as the taste. Chew slowly, savoring the flavor. Put your fork down between each mouthful. Eating more mindfully allows us to more fully enjoy our food and aids proper digestion. In addition, eating slowly gives our stomachs time to register fullness, which reduces overeating.

Watch your every move. Over the next week, before you do anything, ask yourself *why* you are doing it. Is it important? Is it important enough to do right now? A ringing telephone is a perfect example; most people automatically answer the phone without *deciding* to answer it. How much of what you do is action and how much is *re*action?

Listen to what you say. How often do you think or say, "I have to"? Replace these statements with "I choose to." It will relieve a lot of the pressure you place on yourself. And it will give you a whole new perspective.

Look at where you spend your time and energy. Many times, we focus our energy, time, and attention on trivial matters to avoid dealing with larger, more important issues. A preoccupation with keeping a spotless house, for example, may be masking a communication problem in your marriage.

Daily Stress Busters

Take it one day at a time. If that's too much to think about, take it one hour at a time.

Turn those "stress-building" thoughts into "stress-busting" thoughts. When you are under stress, what messages are you sending yourself? You can decrease your stress by learning to talk to yourself in a reassuring way. For example, instead of saying, "I'll never get this assignment done in time" say "If I stay focused and take it one step at a time, I'll make steady progress."

Keep a stress journal. Record each stressful event and rate your perceived level of stress from zero (most relaxed) to 10 (most stressed). Do you see any trends? Do you experience more stress when dealing with people, things, or ideas? Think about what you might be able to do to reduce your stress level next time you experience these stressors.

Write a list of things that make you feel happy and at peace with the world. Do one of those activities today — right now.

Take a breather. Close your eyes and breathe deeply. Clear your mind of all negative thoughts. Imagine yourself in a calm, stress-free environment such as an ocean beach or sitting on a rock alongside a river. Slowly count down from 10, allowing all stress to flow from your mind and body.

Try acting in a way that is the opposite of your usual behavior. For example, if you feel overburdened because of a need to control, delegate a task and take note of what happens.

Are you a people pleaser? Don't let your desire to please others control your life. Try every day to do something to please yourself. It is your choice.

Carefree Mornings

Get a stress-free start each day. If your day starts out stressful, you tend to react more quickly and more often to stress throughout the day. Try replacing your alarm clock buzzer with an alarm clock that has a bulb that gradually brightens to help you awake more naturally. If you typically race around in the morning, lay out your clothes and make your lunch the evening before.

Lift your mind and spirit daily. Use inspirational posters, quotes, and notes, or a screensaver on your computer as a daily reminder of your desire to live a more peaceful life.

Determine your number one priority for the day and do it.

Enjoy Yourself!

Plan a friends' night out. Call your best friend or a few good friends and plan a night (or morning or afternoon) out with no kids and no spouses.

Get away. Pack a bag and retreat to your favorite destination. Or go visit a friend or family member whose company you really enjoy.

Take a wellness day. If you have the benefit of paid personal days or if you can afford to take an unpaid day off, tell your boss you don't need a sick day, but you do need a wellness day to help prevent you from getting sick! Then do whatever your heart desires on that day.

Go to a spa-a-a-h. Treat yourself to a full-body massage, facial, pedicure, or manicure. Leave your worries at the door and enjoy a little bit of heaven on earth.

Send your laundry out. You may not be able to afford to do this every week, but if you are having a particularly hectic week, why not?

Order dinner and a movie. Pick up a video and something to eat on your way home or have dinner delivered and order a pay-per-view movie. Put your feet up and relax.

Use flower power. Have flowers delivered to your home or stop by your local florist and get yourself a big bouquet — it doesn't have to be a special occasion.

Inject some humor into your situation. You may not be able to control what is causing you stress, but you can change your reaction to it. Look for whatever humor may be present. Has a "comedy of errors" led you to your present circumstances? Imagine that you are a stand-up comedian explaining your situation or predicament.

Laugh a little more. Laughter will help you relax — physically and psychologically. Spend time with people who make you laugh. Choose funny movies to watch or read the comic strips in your daily newspaper.

Try yoga. Yoga is the 5,000-year-old remedy for stress. It's an integrated practice of gentle stretching, physical postures, breathing exercises, relaxation techniques, and meditation that can help reduce stress, renew energy, and produce a sense of well-being.

Don't obsess about what you're doing wrong. Think of what you're doing right.

Soothing Rituals

Take two for tea. After washing the dishes or putting the kids to bed, make a cup of chamomile tea. Sit quietly and comfortably as you sip the beverage and allow your body to relax. You can further enhance relaxation by dimming the lights and lighting a few candles.

Take a bath. Add a few drops of essential oil, such as lavender, to your bathwater. Spend at least 20 minutes soaking. Forget about the soap and shampoo. The goal of this bath is not to clean, but just to relax.

Schedule an "electronic blackout." If you want a truly peaceful evening at home, unplug the television, turn off the cellular phone, pager, computer, and fax machine, and turn the volume down on the answering machine.

Massage your brain. By listening to music you switch over from the left hemisphere of your brain to the creative, artistic right hemisphere. The best tunes for relaxation are tunes with relaxed, unhurried rhythms, but any music you find enjoyable can lift your spirits.

Take a catnap. Place an herbal eye pillow over your eyes. Set your alarm for 20 minutes and relax. It doesn't matter if you fall asleep. You should feel more relaxed and refreshed.

Create a sacred place. This can be as simple as a corner of your bedroom with a throw pillow and candle on the floor or as elaborate as a room or an entire house designed using the principles of feng shui. You want to create a quiet, peaceful place in which you can close your eyes and shut out the "busyness" of the world around you.

Once each day, try sitting in complete silence and doing nothing except breathing for 10 minutes.

Eat your meals at the table without the radio or television. Use dinnertime as a time to catch up with other members of the household.

Have some scents. Find some potpourri you like and fill a jar in your bedroom. Put scented sachets in your dresser drawers. Light scented candles.

Spend time outdoors every day. Allow yourself to become part of the scenery. Breathe in the energy of the plant and animal life around you. Allow the sun to melt away your stress, then let the wind blow it away, or give it up to the stars.

> *For a long time it had seemed to me that life was about to begin — real life. But there was always some obstacle in the way, something to be gotten through first, some unfinished business, time still to be served, a debt to be paid. Then, life would begin. At last it dawned on me that these obstacles were my life.*
>
> — Alfred D. Souza

ELIMINATE MENTAL CLUTTER THROUGH MEDITATION

A lot of stress can be traced to the negative "chatter" that goes on in our minds — muddled thoughts about what we said or did or should have said or done, or what we think we might say or do — which only serves to distract us from fully enjoying the present. Meditation provides a welcome break from internal as well as external noise. Consult books, videos, or, better yet, a yoga teacher or other spiritual guide for instructions on meditation exercises your can incorporate into your daily routine.

Slow down. Focus on the quality of your life instead of on getting ahead.

Find a creative outlet. Draw or paint. Make a birthday card with pictures and letters cut out of magazines. Grow a garden. Write a poem or a letter.

Ask yourself what real impact a stressful situation will have on you in a day or a week, and see if you can let the negative thoughts go.

Remember: A thought is just a suggestion. You can choose to go with the thought — and all the emotions that go with it — or not.

ON-LINE HELP FOR STRESS MANAGEMENT

There is a wealth of reliable information on the Internet about all aspects of stress — from what it is to how to manage it in your life. An excellent place to start looking for answers is the Internet Mental Health Web site at www.mentalhealth.com. Also check out the Web site for the International Stress Management Association, located at www.stress-management-isma.org.

Chapter 4

Nurture Relationships

In this chapter . . .
- *Life Support*
- *At Work*
- *Tips for Parents*
- *Managing Anger*

Life Support

Research shows that people who have family and friends to help them through stressful times stay healthier and recover faster than those who do not have a social support system. So hold on tight to family ties and friendships!

Create a support network. Your support network can include family members, friends, coworkers — anyone whom you can turn to for comfort, a sympathetic ear, good ideas, or a more objective opinion. Avoid associations with people whose words and deeds suggest a radical departure from your values.

Make time for people you care about. When was the last time you had a long chat with your best friend? Or hugged your brother or sister? It's so easy to get caught up in doing and achieving that we often neglect to make time to be with the people we love.

If you don't have a furry friend, get one. A study conducted by the State University of New York at Buffalo suggests that sharing your home with a cat or dog can lower blood pressure and keep you calm during times of stress.

Be open to new friendships. If you are lonely, get involved in a worthwhile community project or organization.

Avoid self-pity. Do something to help someone in need.

Improving Communications

Throw out unrealistic expectations of yourself and others. You cannot be all things to all people. Not everyone is going to like you or share your opinion. No one is right all of the time.

Define your limits. Communicate exactly what you can and cannot do. Learn to say "no" without feeling guilty.

Remember the three Rs:
- Respect for self
- Respect for others
- Responsibility for all your actions

Appreciate and accept yourself. If you do, others will too.

Recognize that we're all doing the best we can. If there is someone in your family or office with whom you frequently become frustrated, the next time you interact with that person tell yourself that he or she is doing the best he or she can at this moment in life.

Recognize that you cannot change other people. If someone you care about has a problem, don't make it your problem. Just listen and be there.

Don't be afraid to admit a mistake. Being less than perfect is the common thread of humanity. When you realize that you've made a mistake, take immediate steps to correct it.

Couples & Stress

Problems for most couples begin with differences in style, beliefs, or goals. He's talkative; she's the silent type. He thinks the children should have a religious upbringing; she think the kids should decide for themselves when they get older.

There's no way to avoid all conflicts. Conflicts actually can help strengthen your relationship when you work together to resolve them through effective listening and communication.

Be assertive about your wants and needs. If you are waiting for a loved one to figure out what you might like, be prepared to wait a very long time. Keep requests simple and straightforward and include a time frame, if possible. For example, "Could you please call me as soon as you know that you are going to be running late?"

Compliment your partner every day.

When a problem arises, sit down to discuss it as quickly as possible. Turn off the television. Face each other and hold hands. Start by saying, "I love you and I know that we can resolve this."

Fight right. First, say what's bothering you. Use "I feel" statements about specific behaviors. If you're on the receiving end, listen to the other's feelings without commenting, defending, or disagreeing. Second, discuss the details of your disagreement — this disagreement, not old grievances. Third, negotiate. Both parties need to give and take.

Spend more time together doing things as a couple. Spending time together on a regular basis is a great reminder of why you like each other. And you'll be less likely to argue over the small stuff.

Don't put off getting outside help. If your relationship involves physical or verbal abuse, or drug or alcohol abuse, seek professional help.

At Work

No matter how stressful your work situation is, you can choose to make it less stressful and more satisfying. The following tips can help.

See problems as opportunities. A demanding boss could end up as your biggest supporter. Finding a mistake could prevent you from making an even bigger one.

Enjoy your leisure time. If you spend your non-working hours doing things you enjoy, you'll have a much better state of mind during your regular working hours.

Take a problem out to lunch. Sometimes, our best efforts are thwarted by people who don't necessarily mean to trip us up. For example, you may be doing great work on the job, but someone else keeps taking all the credit. Once a month, take your number one "human problem" out to breakfast or lunch and frankly discuss what's bothering you. Keep the conversation focused not on the person's behavior but on how that behavior makes you feel.

State your intention to remain calm. Make the decision when you wake up each morning that you are going to remain calm and peaceful at work. You'll feel better for it, and your serenity may rub off on your co-workers.

Work at your own pace. Try not to compare yourself to others.

Improve your time management skills. You can make your workload appear lighter by learning how to prioritize your work and manage your time better.

Tips for Parents

Leave stress at work. Studies have shown that if Mom or Dad comes home grumpy from work, the stress and negative emotions can infect the whole family like chicken pox. If you've had a bad day, do something on the way home to improve your mood. Listen to soothing music in your car or take a brisk walk.

Establish family routines for getting up, going to bed, eating meals, doing homework, and socializing. Stick to these routines as much as possible.

Set rules with — not for — your teenager.

Let children in on planning how you spend family time and money.

Reward good behavior with kind words. Praise accomplishments and express your appreciation through simple statements such as "I really appreciate how you . . ." or "It was great that you . . ."

Hold weekly family meetings. It's important to set aside a time when family members are encouraged and expected to share feelings and concerns. Let children suggest solutions to problems that are brought up in family meetings.

REMAIN IN CONTROL

The next time you start losing your patience, try some of these tips from the National Committee to Prevent Child Abuse:

- Press your lips together and count to 10 or higher, if needed.
- Take several deep breaths. Remember, you are the adult.
- Close your eyes. Pretend you're hearing what your child is about to hear.
- Put your child in a time-out chair (one minute for each year of age).
- Put yourself in a time-out chair. Think about why you are angry. Is it really your child, or is your child simply a convenient target for your anger?
- Phone a friend.
- If your child is old enough to be home alone, tell him or her that you are going for a walk and that you will want to discuss his or her behavior when you get back.
- Splash water on your face.
- Hug a pillow.

Take time to listen. When you listen, it makes others feel valued and loved. Never refuse a request to talk with a child or spouse.

Help your children feel loved. Spend time with them, show affection, use caring discipline, and set limits. When children feel loved, they are better able to cope with stress.

Managing Anger

Recent studies suggest that venting your anger may be as damaging to your health as keeping it all inside. Reflective coping is a technique for managing anger that involves acknowledging your anger, but waiting until your "hot thoughts" have cooled so that you can rationally discuss the situation that gave rise to your anger.

Talk honestly about what's bothering you with the object of your frustration at a time when you can discuss it calmly and rationally. If you need to, write down some of your key concerns so that you don't forget to bring them up.

Work together toward a solution. Ask each person to state the problem from his or her point of view. Ask questions if you don't understand. Then have each person come up with a few ideas for solving the conflict. Assume that you share a common interest: the desire for a friendly outcome.

Attack the behavior, not the person. If someone's behavior is upsetting to you, make a simple statement such as, "When you [do whatever it is he or she is doing], I feel [whatever it is you are feeling]" and then wait for a response. While their first instinct may be to defend themselves, very often, when people learn that their behavior is causing someone undue stress, they will want to change that behavior.

Be understanding. Put yourself in the other person's shoes. What would satisfy her? What does she want?

Avoid criticizing. It makes people feel inferior, which makes them angry.

Chapter 5

Gain Financial Freedom

In this chapter . . .

- *Budgeting and Spending*
- *Reduce Your Debt*
- *Savings and Investments*
- *Living on Less*
- *Creative Frugality*
- *Frugal Family Fun*
- *Frugal Grown-up Fun*

Money may well be at the heart of your stress. Gaining control of your finances is the first step to financial freedom. You may never achieve financial independence, but you can take steps to reduce your debt (and spending) and increase your savings and investments so that you don't have to worry so much about money. *That's* financial freedom.

What are your beliefs about money? Is money an end in itself or a means to something? How much is enough? Many people are discovering that less is more. The less you spend, the less you need to work. And the less you have to work, the more time you have for the things that really matter.

Budgeting and Spending

The best way to figure out where your money goes is to keep track of every penny you spend for an entire month. It's helpful if you use a form like the one on pages 64 and 65. Fill out a form each week for one month and then total what you spent in each category. Once you know where all your money is going, you can develop a realistic budget that is much easier to maintain.

Making Budgets Work

Resist the urge to have immediate gratification. Change your mind-set from "I want it now" to "If I wait, there's something better I can have later."

Stick to your budget. Once you have established a realistic budget, make a conscientious effort to stick to it for at least three months. At the end of each month, compare your budget figures to actual figures. If you are way off course after the first month, see if you can make a couple of adjustments during the next month to bring those numbers closer together. After a few months, you should need to make only minor adjustments.

Shopping for a car? Consider buying a good used car instead of a new car. Use the money you save by having a lower car payment to reduce your debt, or put the money toward savings and investments each month.

WHERE DOES ALL YOUR MONEY GO?				
EXPENSE	**DAY 1**	**DAY 2**	**DAY 3**	
Gasoline				
Eating Out				
Entertainment				
Food at Work				
Groceries				
Clothing				
Gifts/Cards				
Dry Cleaning				
Personal Items				
Magazines/Newspapers				
Car Payment				
Mortgage Payment				
Credit Card Payment				
Loan Payment				
Other				
Total				

Try the cash system for nonbill expenses. Create separate envelopes for groceries, gas, entertainment, and other regularly occurring expenses. Each week, put into these envelopes the cash amount you have budgeted for each expense. Borrow cash from another expense envelope only if you are absolutely sure that you will not need it for that expense.

	Day 4	Day 5	Day 6	Day 7	Total

Are you paying too much for your own money? Automatic teller machines (ATMs) are a wonderfully convenient way to access your money, but ATM fees can add up. Make it a point to find and use ATMs that do not charge you for your own money. Or if you have been going to the ATM three times a week, take out your usual weekly withdrawal once a week or even biweekly so you have one fee instead of three or more.

Make a few little cutbacks. Look at your spending over the past week. Where might you be able to cut back on spending without affecting the quality of your life? Many people spend $5 a day or more on lunches. That's $1,300 a year! You could save money by bringing your lunch from home.

Look for "cash cushions." Money above and beyond the amount needed to pay monthly bills and expenses often gets frittered away. Use it toward debt reduction or savings.

Save before you spend. Arrange for automatic transfers from your paycheck to an investment or savings account. Doing this will give you more security and, ultimately, financial freedom.

Know the difference between wants and needs. We *need* food, water, shelter, and clothing. We *want* gourmet meals, big-screen televisions, fancy cars, and stylish apparel. Before you go shopping for a particular item, ask yourself whether it is something you need or something you want. If it's a luxury item and you really "must" have it, develop a budget for it.

No-Fuss Bill Paying

Use the list method. Another way to manage payments is to put all unpaid bills in a "To Be Paid" folder with a list of each bill, the amount due, and

LET YOUR CREDIT CARDS PAY YOU

If credit cards are a necessity, choose cards that pay you to use them. Credit cards like the Discover Card offer cash back on total annual purchases. If you use it for everything (groceries, gas, restaurants, travel, and so on), you get back a little something every year to add to your savings or investment fund. The key is to pay off your balance every month; otherwise the interest you pay will far outweigh the cash you get back. And be sure to choose a card that does not charge an annual fee.

the due date. As you pay each bill, cross it off the list. Add new bills to the bottom of the list. Write check numbers on paid bills and file in folders designated for each specific category: for example, telephone, car insurance.

Pay bills twice a month. Use a folder with two pockets — one for bills to be paid on the first of the month and one for bills to be paid on the fifteenth. Keep this folder handy so that you can put bills into the appropriate pocket right when they arrive.

Fill a three-ring binder with pocket folders for filing receipts and bills by category. You can easily keep track of payments by writing the check number, amount, and date paid on each folder. This method is especially handy if you have a lot of household expenses that are tax deductible, because you'll have everything in one place when tax time rolls around. And it eliminates filing monthly bills.

Spend Wisely

Look at the real cost of your purchases. Think in terms of how many hours you need to work to pay for each item you want to buy. For example, if you earn $15 an hour and an item costs $120, ask yourself if you would be willing to work eight hours to have that item.

Trade credit cards for debit cards. A debit card combines the convenience of a credit card with the sensibleness of paying cash. Debit cards are different from credit cards, as they are tied to cash in a bank account. They are particularly useful for making airline, hotel, or car rental reservations over the telephone.

Use only cash when shopping. When you shop with cash, you put more thought into each purchase. And you don't have to spend any time wondering if you can really afford something: Either you have enough cash or you don't.

Reduce Your Debt

You don't need to make more money to reduce your debt. You simply need to change what you do with the money you have. Keep reading.

Getting Out of Credit Card Debt

Take a good look at your credit card statements. About 30 to 40 percent of your minimum monthly payment goes toward interest, and only 60 to 70 percent goes toward reducing your actual debt. So if your minimum monthly payment is $50, you're paying $15 to $20 every month for nothing.

Even if you don't charge another thing on your credit cards, it can take a surprising number of years to pay off what you owe when you pay only the minimum amount due each month. Here's a foolproof plan for getting rid of credit card debt.

1. List your debts in order of the lowest to highest amounts owed. Use whatever money you have freed up in your budgeting process to pay extra toward the first debt on your list.
2. Pay the minimum amount due on the other debts. Continue to do this each month until the first debt on your list is paid. Here's where you really start making progress.
3. Combine the amount you've been paying on the first debt to the minimum monthly amount due on the next debt until it, too, is paid. Continue this process until all debt is paid.
4. Begin to apply your total debt reduction payment each month to savings and investments.

Make payments on time every month. If you make even one late payment or skip a payment one month, many credit card companies will increase your interest rate dramatically. So it will take even longer to pay off your debt. If you must, make a late payment to a more lenient creditor, such as the telephone or electric company.

Use bankruptcy as a last resort. Filing for bankruptcy may seem like an easy out, but a bankruptcy remains on your credit report for 10 years and will affect your ability to secure a loan for a car or home. It also may rear its ugly head in a routine employment check and cost you a job.

Pay attention to notices on your bill. Some credit companies will try to raise your interest rate for no reason at all. But they are required by law to notify you in advance and give you the option of declining the higher rate of interest. Exercising this option generally requires writing a letter to the address they provide. Do it.

Pare down to one credit card. Reducing the number of credit cards you have can cut your debt and simplify your life with fewer bills to pay.

Avoid debt traps. If you are paying on a credit card or loan, you may receive credit checks from time to time with an enticement to use them to go on a well-deserved vacation, install a backyard pool for some summertime fun, or simply give yourself a nice cash bonus. Don't do it; it's a debt trap. Rip up the checks (so no one else can use them) and throw them away immediately.

Don't try ducking creditors. You'll actually buy yourself more time if you settle on an amount and show that you are willing to repay your debt. If you are having difficulty making minimum monthly payments, contact the Consumer Credit Counseling Service in your area (check your Yellow Pages or call toll-free information).

Freeze your credit — literally. If you tend to overspend on credit, put your credit cards in a small plastic tub filled with water and place the tub in the freezer. Freezing your credit cards will curb impulse credit card shopping by helping you make a conscious choice about what and when you will buy on credit. Once you get used to buying with cash (and you see your credit card balances going down), you may want to thaw and then cut up those credit cards.

Close unused credit accounts. It's a good idea to cancel credit cards that are paid in full for two reasons. First, it will keep you from getting sucked back into charging. Second, the credit card companies will notify the credit reporting agencies, and your credit file will be updated.

This is important because having too much open credit could result in a loan denial for a major purchase, such as a home or car.

Don't use credit to pay back credit. If you're short one month, you may be tempted to take a cash advance on one credit card to pay the monthly

What Is the Real Cost of Debt?

There is a great on-line publication called *bankrate.com* that is an excellent source of articles and information to help you manage your credit. The Web site includes a debt repayment calculator that figures the real cost of your debt; that is, how much you end up paying in interest.

Go to www.bankrate.com and click on "Credit Cards." Then click on "Cost of Debt" to bring up the calculator. Enter the total balance of each credit card or loan and the rate of interest you pay for each. Then enter the number of years in which you want to pay off the balance. This will give you the amount you need to pay each month to achieve your goal. The calculator also lets you compare the total interest you pay — or the real cost of your debt — based on the length of the loan.

payment due on another card. Don't do it! You're just digging yourself deeper into debt.

Don't blow a windfall. If you receive a tax refund or any other significant sum of cash, resist the urge to spend it. Apply the whole thing toward a debt and you'll be free that much sooner from monthly payments.

Savings and Investments

If you have a steady job, chances are very good that you're spending money as fast as you earn it and that you have a hard time keeping yourself from dipping into your savings for this and that. You might not be worried now about what you're going to live on when you retire, but the sooner you start putting money away, the more money you'll have when the time comes. Here are a few ideas to get you started.

Build for the Future

Make your money work harder. Consider moving money from traditional savings and money market accounts to certificates of deposit. A certificate of deposit allows you to deposit a certain amount of money as an investment for a fixed length of time, ranging from three months to five years. CDs are federally insured and pay much higher rates of return.

Pay yourself first. Before you start writing out checks for bills, make a payment to a savings or investment account. Make it a habit to save something each month — even if it's only $10. Increase that amount as you pay off debts or get pay raises.

Live within your means by using the 70-20-10 rule. Use 70 percent of your take-home pay for regular monthly bills plus other regular expenses such as groceries, gas, tuition, and clothing. Set aside 20 percent for large-ticket items such as a car or home. Save the remaining 10 percent. This will help keep you from overextending yourself with credit.

Spend less, invest more. Use automatic payments from your paycheck (or your checking or savings account) to fund investment contributions and learn to live on what's left rather than overspending and finding yourself unable to make regular contributions.

Contribute annually to an IRA. The government allows a tax deduction of up to $2,000 a year ($4,000 if you file jointly) when you invest in a regular Individual Retirement Account (IRA). Your investment will grow tax-deferred until you begin to withdraw at retirement. Check with your tax specialist for options, restrictions, and eligibility requirements.

Fund your 401(k) to the max. If your company offers a 401(k) program, take full advantage of it. Automatic deductions from your paycheck make it a painless way to save for retirement. Some companies even offer to match part of your contribution, which really helps your balance grow.

Invest all extra income. Whether you get a nice tax refund or raise or win the lottery, plan to invest any extra cash that comes your way rather than spend it.

Use CDs to save for large expenditures. Plan ahead and sock away money for vacation or holidays.

Involve the whole family in saving. Ask family members to think of ways they can save money each week. Keep a chart of the money saved so that you can monitor your progress. Offer a reward, such as a family trip, for reaching the goal.

Look at the little picture. Let's say, for example, that you want to save $2,000 over the next year. That works out to $5.48 a day. Now look at your daily expenses. Where might you be able to cut back by $5.48 each day? Start putting away that amount — in cash — every day. At the end of the week, take your saved money to the bank and deposit it in your savings account.

Save your loose change. Get into the habit — and encourage family members to get in the habit — of putting all loose change in a jar every night. At the end of the week, roll up your change and deposit it in your savings account.

Living on Less

If you are struggling to make ends meet, you can reclaim control over your finances — and your life — by choosing to consume less. Consuming less also saves trees, mineral resources, water, and the environment.

Reducing Food Costs

Take out instead of eating out. When you eat out, you have to add an extra 15 to 20 percent to the bill for service, and you pay a ridiculous price for beverages. Ordering takeout allows you to save on the "added costs" of eating out while enjoying the same quality of food.

Eat out less. If you eat out once a week, make it once a month. Too tired to cook at night? Cook large meals on the weekends and eat leftovers during the week. And use your slow cooker! Prepare ingredients the night before and throw them into the pot before leaving for work. Coming home to a hot meal is like having a cook. And you have only one pot to wash.

Plan ahead and save on lunch costs. Make up a week's worth of sandwiches on the weekend and freeze them in separate plastic bags, then place them all in a large airtight bag. Remove sandwiches from the freezer each morning, and they will be defrosted by lunchtime. Fillings that freeze well include peanut butter, ham, bologna, salami, turkey, chicken, pastrami, roast beef or pork, and tuna mixed with sour cream or salad dressing. Mayonnaise, cheese, and jelly do not freeze well.

Buy food in bulk. Stock up on canned goods when they go on sale. Buy large bags of flour, sugar, rice, pasta, and beans from your local food cooperative or wholesale club. Not enough storage space in your kitchen? Store it in your basement or garage (providing they are dry), out of the reach of potential pests. Make room in a linen closet, bathroom cupboard, or hallway closet. Or store extra supplies under your bed in labeled boxes, with the labels facing out.

Eat out earlier in the day. If you enjoy going out to eat but don't enjoy paying the high price of a gourmet dinner, go out for a gourmet brunch or lunch instead for about half the price — or less.

Grow a vegetable garden. Plan meals around what's in season. Trade produce with neighbors and coworkers.

Eat vegetarian more often. Eating meat less often will reduce your food bill considerably. Substitute main dishes that feature eggs, beans, cheese, or tofu as a source of protein.

Saving — Simply

Take care of what you own. When you buy items, choose high quality over low price. High-quality, high-efficiency, durable goods will last longer and can be repaired if necessary.

Buy only out of need, such as to replace something that is used up, worn out, or broken beyond repair.

Donate clothes to charity and deduct the expense from your income taxes. For every $100 worth of clothing you donate, you could save yourself 15 to 33 percent in taxes at the end of the year. Just be sure to keep a list of the items you donate, along with the value of each item, and ask for a tax-deductible receipt from the charity to which you donate. *Note:* This works only if you itemize your taxes.

Learn to want what you have. Look at the many things you own. Do you wear all of your jewelry and clothes? Probably not. Do you use all the gadgets in your kitchen? Probably not. Do you have more material possessions than your parents and grandparents did? Probably. Be thankful for the abundance in your life.

Get cash for clothes you aren't wearing by selling them on consignment. Clothes must be in excellent condition and relatively new or classically styled. Typically, there is a 60- to 90-day contract period in which your clothes will be for sale in the shop, and the seller (that's you) gets 40 to 50 percent of the selling price. *Bonus tip:* Make even more money by picking up good, cheap clothes at yard sales and then selling them on consignment.

Get rid of a car. If you have one car that is not driven every day, compare the cost of owning a car with the cost of renting a car or taking a cab on the occasions when you need a vehicle.

STOP JUNK MAIL!

How often do you get offers in the mail that happen to be something you were looking for? More often than not, it's seeing a product or offer that makes us think we want it. To stop junk mail, write to:

> Mail Preference Service
> Direct Marketing Association
> P.O. Box 9008
> Farmingdale, NY 11735-9008

Allow several months for the deluge to subside. Meanwhile, make a commitment to throw out every catalog and direct-mail offer without even opening it.

Save on holiday gifts and seasonal items. Buy greeting cards, wrapping paper, and seasonal decorations at half price right after the holidays. For very inexpensive gifts, look for almost-new items at garage sales, secondhand stores, consignment shops, and thrift shops. Or start early and make your own gifts.

Avoid impulse buying. Shop with a list, and stick to what's on your list. If you see something else you want, resist the urge to buy it on the spot. Go home and think about it for a few days and then decide if it's worth going back for.

Tune out commercial messages. Advertising creates desire. Use commercial breaks to get up and stretch, do a couple of quick household chores, or simply turn down the volume and talk to other members of your household.

> *To live content within small means: to seek elegance rather than luxury and refinement rather than fashion; to be worthy, not respectable, and wealthy, not rich; to listen to stars and birds, to babies and sages with open heart; in a word, to let the spiritual unbidden and unconscious grow up through the common.*
>
> — Ralph Waldo Emerson

Learn to do it yourself. If you can do some of your own repairs or make things you might normally buy, you can save quite a lot of money. See if you can find someone who is willing to teach you what you need to learn. Your local high school or community college may offer continuing education classes. Or teach yourself using books from the library.

Rent videos instead of going to the movies. Save even more by choosing movies that have been out for a while rather than new releases.

Cash in on Specials

Take advantage of membership discounts. Many organizations and associations frequently offer member discounts on a variety of products and services, but most people don't use them because they forget that they are available. Write down on a slip of paper all of the discounts available to you and then carry it in your wallet or purse as a reminder.

Take advantage of off-peak discounts. Some museums offer free admission on certain days of the week. Attend a movie matinee instead of a prime-time show and save some cash. Look for restaurants that offer early-bird dinner specials (usually between 4 P.M. and 6 P.M.). Attend plays on weeknights instead of weekends or go to a preview performance.

Buy movie tickets in bulk. Many movie theater chains offer tickets by mail, which allows you to save about 40 percent off the regular price. Ask your local theater.

Creative Frugality

Are you aware of all the free and reduced-cost activities and items available to you? There are numerous opportunities out there — if you know where to look. All it takes is a little creative thinking and the desire to have fun for free!

Trade baby-sitting services. If you and your significant other would like to have the house to yourselves for the night (a priceless treat!), make arrangements ahead of time to have your children spend the night with friends or family members, with the understanding that you will take in their children another night.

If you can't beat 'em, join 'em. Kids love fast food, but even fast food can get expensive. Why not try re-creating your kids' favorite fast food entrée at home? Betsy Sullivan, editor of *Balancing Act,* a frugality newsletter, tells the story of how she and her boys succeeded in creating a chicken fajita that tasted very much like the one served at McDonald's. They bought one chicken fajita, took it home, pulled it apart, and figured out how to make it. And they had a great time doing it!

Decorate for free. Some local libraries loan out framed paintings and other works of art. All you need is a valid library card and you can bring home a "new" painting or two every month. Seashells, unusual rocks, pinecones, and other natural artifacts can be displayed in canning jars and baskets or made into an artistic arrangement. And, of course, there's nothing like a bouquet of wildflowers to brighten a room.

See plays and concerts for free. Many theaters and concert halls recruit volunteer ushers, who get to enjoy the performance once everyone is seated. Volunteers may even get to meet the performers!

Vacation at home. It's simpler, less expensive, and can be far more relaxing than jetting (or driving) to and from a vacation destination. Create an itinerary just as you would for a regular vacation. Plan to see the local sights that visitors come to see. Try out a new restaurant or two. Order takeout or have food delivered on other nights. Stock up on your favorite breakfast foods, snacks, and beverages. Unplug the telephone, television, and computer. Leave housework for when you "get back." You're on vacation!

Frugal Family Fun

Extend your creative frugality into activities for the whole family. There is so much no- and low-cost entertainment, if you know where to look.

Let the Good Times Roll

You don't have to spend a lot of money for kids to have fun. Check your local newspaper for upcoming events and activities — free festivals, fairs, and other forms of entertainment — that offer frugal fun for the whole family.

Let your kids camp out in the backyard for memories that will last a lifetime.

GREAT FAMILY FUN IDEAS ON-LINE

Whether you're looking for indoor or outdoor activities, arts and crafts ideas, or fun learning activities, you'll find hundreds of tips and ideas on-line. Go to www.momsonline.com and click on "Hot Tips." At this Web site, you'll also find general money-saving tips, plus lots of valuable information for parents.

For a variety of fun learning activities, check out the Family Education Network at www.familyeducation.com. Select an age group and then click on an activity topic. You also can sign up for a free e-mail newsletter.

Another Web site that lets you select activities by age group is ParentTime, which can be found at www.pathfinder.com/parenttime. At Parent Soup (www.parentsoup.com), click on "Education Central" and then "Fun Learning."

Plant a vegetable garden. Kids love to watch things grow, especially if they have a hand in planting and caring for them. Bonus: Once those veggies are ready to pick, you save on produce!

Bring your own. If you plan a trip to an amusement park or other venue that charges exorbitant prices for food and beverages, don't blow your hard-earned money on expensive drinks and snacks. Load a child's wagon with a small cooler and tow it along with you. If there's enough room, young children can ride in the wagon when they get tired.

Take a walk — and talk. Sure, the exercise will do you all good, but the most important benefit of this activity is that it allows you to give your kids what they crave more than anything — your attention. Let them talk about whatever is on their minds.

Take a camping trip. Hotel stays and eating out make up the bulk of expenses on vacation. Camping and cookouts minimize those expenses and add fun and adventure to your trip.

Allow kids to become bored. When kids get bored, their imaginations kick in and they come up with truly creative ways to entertain themselves. It's a wonderful way to help children develop and enhance creativity, imagination, and resourcefulness.

Enjoy simple pleasures as a family. Chances are good that the pace of life for your kids is far more hectic than it was for you when you were their age. Following are some ideas for slowing down the pace with some simple, old-fashioned fun:

- Pick your own apples or berries.
- Bake cookies or cupcakes.
- Play board games.
- Go fly a kite.
- Build a fort — indoors or outdoors.
- Have a neighborhood sidewalk drawing contest.
- Take a family bike ride.
- Bring a picnic lunch to the beach.
- Rent a rowboat on a nearby lake.
- Schedule a family reading hour.
- Put on a play or skit.

Visit your library. Many libraries offer a variety of free activities for children of all ages, including:

- Weekly storytelling hours for children
- Summer reading clubs for children
- Writing workshops

See what's happening at bookstores. Like libraries, many bookstores offer a variety of free activities for children, including:

- Children's video release parties
- Storytelling times
- Young readers' clubs

Frugal Grown-up Fun

Sure, kids are easily amused, but that doesn't mean there isn't a variety of low-cost activities for you "big kids" too. Scan local newspapers, as well as ads and brochures on community bulletin boards, to find out what's happening in your area.

Plan a picnic. Pack a basket, knapsack, or cooler with the makings of a gourmet brunch, lunch, or dinner — complete with the beverages of your choice. Don't forget to bring along a blanket or cloth to spread on the ground.

Give yourself a visitor's tour. Go to your nearest visitors center and pick up some local-interest brochures or ask about fun things to do. Choose places and activities that are new to you.

INTERNET TRAVEL BARGAINS

Go to www.smarterliving.com to sign up for free e-mail newsletters that alert you to deals on airfares, hotels, and car rentals as well as last-minute travel deals from the cities you preselect. When you sign up for the free newsletters, you automatically become a member, which entitles you to discounts on car rentals. The Web site also includes links to other useful sites for requesting visitor guides, weather reports, and maps of your destination.

Throw potluck dinner parties. If you enjoy entertaining but want to keep the cost down, invite friends to a potluck dinner party. Ask them to bring their favorite dish. You can request specific courses or just see what kind of dinner develops!

Visit your local library. Larger public libraries offer a variety of programs and services that are free and open to the public, including:

- Free Internet access
- Writing workshops
- How-to demonstrations and mini seminars
- Book and poetry readings
- Book discussion groups
- Current magazines and newspapers
- Special-interest exhibits
- Free video- and audiocassette loans

Check out what's happening at bookstores. Many bookstores, especially those with cafés, offer a regular schedule of events and activities, including:

- Book and poetry readings
- Writers groups
- Book discussion groups
- Free live music
- Special-interest discussions

Lighten Your Load

In this chapter . . .

- *Unclutter Your Home*
- *Let It Go*
- *Lighten Up!*
- *Free Up Time*

Into each life, a little clutter must fall. But that doesn't mean you have to hold on to it forever! If your life feels out of balance, you might want to lighten your load; that is, free up time, space, and energy for more important things.

Start by paring down your material possessions to those things you either love or use regularly. Lighten your mind by learning to minimize stress. Lighten your heart by letting go of guilt, anger, and other negative emotions and adding more humor and laughter. You'll be healthier and happier for it.

Unclutter Your Home

How much is enough? Do you really need 23 pairs of shoes? Or seven sets of sheets for your bed? Or that handy-dandy gadget you just saw advertised on television? How many things that you have bought are still in your home but not being used?

Acquiring things has become such a habit that we often don't consider the cost of acquisition. Think about the price you pay — not just the cost of purchasing, but also the cost of owning. Material possessions cost you storage space, and they cost you the time it takes to shop and care for them. The more you own, the more you have to care for.

No matter how much you acquire, you will never have it all. Better to have a few possessions that you love and use than a thousand that weigh you down.

Get Back to Basics

There's no right way to unclutter your home and no one way that works for everyone. What's important to remember is that *getting* started is far more important than *how* you get started!

Do not try to unclutter your whole house at once. Work in one room at a time and don't switch to another room until you're done. Seeing progress will motivate you to keep up the good work.

Clean out one drawer each night. You will make progress toward your goal each day and it won't seem like such a huge project.

Plan uncluttering activities around garbage days or plan to take stuff to the dump or your selected charity that day. Otherwise, you may be tempted to reconsider.

Start with the easy stuff. This will get you into the act of uncluttering with little or no pain or anxiety. Get a large garbage bag and walk through your house. Throw out anything that is clearly garbage:

- Expired medicines
- Expired coupons
- Outdated clothes
- Makeup that's more than one year old
- Sunscreen that's more than two years old
- Things that are broken (unless they are valuable and fixable)
- Odd socks
- Grocery bags (10 is enough!)
- Old restaurant and shopping guides
- Outdated calendars
- Spoiled food
- Rusted utensils and tools
- Travel literature and maps (unless they are new and you have definite plans to travel in the next three months)

Sort belongings into three categories: what you definitely use, what you definitely don't use, and things you can't separate into either of those categories. Put away the things you use. Give away the things you don't use. Store in boxes those things you probably don't use but can't part with just yet. If in six months you haven't opened your boxes, give the items away.

Start with a single drawer. Empty the contents so you can see everything. Pick up each item and make a decision. If you haven't used or needed that item in the last year or simply don't like or want it anymore, put it in a trash bag. Organize what's left by putting like things together in a box or using rubber bands or plastic bags to contain them.

DETERMINING WHAT TO KEEP

As you decide the relative merit of each item, ask yourself the following questions:

- When was the last time I used this?
- Why don't I use it more often?
- Does it have any sentimental value?
- Do I love it?
- What is the worst possible thing that could happen if I just threw it away? Can I live with that?
- Could I get another one if I needed to?
- If I keep it, where should it go?
- How many of these do I need?

Where to Put It

Designate one room or space for all papers. This is where you pay bills and file them. That way, when you're looking for a particular piece of paperwork, you have automatically narrowed down your search.

Look for hiding places — for your clutter, not you! Store extra table leaves under your sofa and linens in boxes under your bed. Use decorative screens and curtains to hide cluttered areas.

Store things where you use them. For instance, if you keep your bathroom cleaning supplies under the bathroom sink, it makes it easy to tackle the job at any time and eliminates unnecessary steps. Rearrange kitchen cabinets so that glasses and plates are near the dishwasher.

Let It Go

It makes sense that when we're feeling happy and peaceful, we want to hold on to our happiness or peaceful state forever. But why are we so reluctant to let go of unhappy emotions? Letting go doesn't mean suppressing emotions; that's like putting an adhesive bandage on a serious wound. Sure, you can't see it when you cover it up, but it's still festering underneath the bandage. And it just keeps getting worse. The same is true for emotional wounds.

It's important to air negative feelings and mistakes — and then let them go so that you can heal.

Learning How to Release

Identify the fear. Anger is a defense mechanism in response to a perceived danger or threat. When you are angry, ask yourself what you are frightened of. If someone is angry with you, try to figure out what might be frightening that person. The best thing you can do is to show compassion.

Learn your lesson. People often say, "Things happen for a reason." When something upsetting happens, think about why it happened to you and why it happened at this particular time in your life. What have you learned or gained from this experience?

Don't get even; get angry. If you can't express your anger to the party that has angered you, stand in front of a mirror and express it to yourself. Let it all out and then let it go.

Shed some inhibitions. Articulate a "taboo" or fear and then break it. For instance, if you've never gone to the movies alone, try it. If you are afraid of a particular item or activity, read up on the subject and then look for an opportunity to be exposed to your fear — without fearing for your safety. Enlist the aid of a trusted friend or a professional.

Forgive yourself, and forgive others. Take a deep breath and exhale the guilt, anger, and resentment. What's done is done. Is there any way you can make amends? Until you can forgive what happened in the past, you cannot live freely and joyfully in the present. Don't waste another second of precious life imprisoned in the past; forgive and forget, or at least forgive and move on.

Close your eyes and imagine that you are riding on the wings of an angel. From this great distance, you see your physical self way down below. You notice that wherever you go, whatever you do, there's a dark cloud directly over your head. The cloud is so full of negative emotions (anger, guilt, or frustration) that they are beginning to rain down on you and that's all you can feel. Something inside (or was it the voice of your angel?) urges you to take a deep breath and blow away that cloud. See the "poof" of your breath as it pushes the dark cloud away. Watch it vanish into thin air and then feel the sunlight begin to warm you from the inside out. Enjoy the light for a few minutes before opening your eyes and rejoining with your loving self.

> *Forgiving can be the beginning of the healing process. We must remember that hatred is like acid. It does more damage to the vessel in which it is stored than to the object on which it is poured.*
>
> — Ann Landers

Lighten Up!

Many aspects of everyday living are serious, but that doesn't mean you can't look for the humor in life. Allow yourself to enjoy your family, friends, and surroundings, and your life will be all the richer for it.

Guarantee more fun in your life. Put yourself in situations you enjoy and in the company of people you enjoy.

Take time to play. If you're walking past a playground, stop and swing awhile. Or take a trip down the slide.

When in doubt, laugh. Let it out. A good belly laugh not only feels good, but it also gives your abdominal muscles a good workout, along with easing tension and stress.

Spare yourself the clutter caused by bad feelings. Participate in activities that make you feel good; eliminate or reduce your participation in activities that don't.

Don't take yourself so seriously. Make a funny face in the mirror. Now make a *really* funny face.

Put things into perspective. Rate what happens to you on a scale of 1 to 10. Not everything is an 8, 9, or 10. Save your energy for the truly big stuff.

Double your happiness: Share it!

Learn to roll with the punches. Think of someone you know who always seems to be happy, no matter what happens. There's something he or she is doing that's different from what you are doing in response to life's punches. See if you can figure out what it is. Or ask, "What's your secret?"

Change Your Point of View

Go with the flow. Being flexible allows greater enjoyment of today. An appointment that gets canceled, for example, is an opportunity to enjoy some unexpected free time.

Adjust your attitude. When you are faced with one of life's lessons in patience, such as a traffic jam or a long line at the checkout, remember that while you may have no control over the situation, your attitude is always within your control. You can choose to be angry and frustrated, or you can choose to remain calm and relaxed. Strike up a conversation with a total stranger. Or entertain yourself by looking at the people around you and making up stories about their lives.

Sing and dance away negative emotions. In using voice and movement, we free negative energy that is stored within our bodies. Go ahead and put on your favorite music and sing or dance to it. If you've got a good imagination, pretend that you're a famous performer in front of a very receptive audience. Don't forget to take a bow!

State your intention to do better. If it is difficult for you to let go of negative emotions, create an affirmation to help you. Your affirmation might be something like "I am a loving, forgiving person" or "My heart radiates the healing energy of forgiveness." Repeat your affirmation aloud a few times every day.

Free Up Time

Research shows that Americans (with the exception of parents with young children) have about 40 more hours of free time each week than previous generations. According to Geoff Godbey, a professor of leisure studies at the Pennsylvania State University and coauthor of *Time for Life,* about 25 hours of free time come during weekdays, usually in 30- to 45-minute increments. But the typical American estimates his or her weekly amount of free time at 19 hours. Perhaps that is because we watch an average of 16 to 21 hours of television each week! Just think of what you might be able to do and enjoy with that extra 20 hours or so of free time each week.

Waste Not, Want Not

Harness your energy. Whether it's first thing in the morning or late at night, there's a time of day that is generally your most productive time. Use this time to accomplish those things that require the largest amount of energy or brainpower.

Watch your television time. How often do you sit down to watch one show and end up watching several hours of television? Try turning the television on a half hour later than usual or turning it off a half hour earlier, and then take that time to do something else. Better yet, don't turn the television on unless there is a specific show you want to see and then turn it off when that show is over.

Do the worst task first. Get the least pleasurable task out of the way, and then the time in the rest of your day is free from worrying or thinking about it.

Fight back against procrastination. Think of procrastination as a crime that steals your time. Get tough on yourself. When you find yourself procrastinating, will yourself to stop what you're doing and begin what you need to be doing. If you do this consistently over a period of a few weeks, you will not only make better use of your time, but you will have more time left over each day as well.

Use your lunch hour productively. If you have an hour for lunch, plan to spend 30 minutes eating and 30 minutes doing something that you want or need to do such as:

- Read a book.
- Take a nap.
- Take a walk.
- Pick up a few groceries.
- Make personal phone calls.
- Write a letter.
- Run a couple of quick errands.
- Just sit and think about whatever.

Save yourself worry. Don't waste time trying to change things over which you have no control. Adapt your response if necessary, but accept the things you cannot change and move on.

Let someone else do your grocery shopping. Grocery shopping services are popping up in cities all over the United States. You can order via telephone, fax, or on-line. You can't use coupons, but prices are fairly competitive and the service will deliver a minimum order for free at a time that's convenient for you.

Remind yourself every once in a while that all you really *must* do today is breathe in and breathe out. Nobody's going to die if you don't get everything on your list done today.

Plan on leftovers. On the weekend or whenever you have more time, double or quadruple a recipe and freeze the leftovers for a quick, nutritious meal on a busier night. If you do this regularly, you'll spend a fraction of the time you spend now on cooking, which will free up more time to pursue other things.

Prioritize Now

Include on your "to do" list a realistic estimate of the time you will need to complete that activity or task. This will keep you from overcommitting.

Assess your priorities. How do you determine your priorities? By asking yourself:

- What makes me happy?
- What is the one thing I most want to accomplish?
- What do I value most?

Stay focused. Whether you're trying to unclutter a closet or write up a report at work, make a conscious choice to stick with it until the job is done. If it's an extensive project, decide before you begin how long you will work before taking a break or moving to another project. Limit distractions by turning off the telephone ringer or closing your door. The sooner you finish, the more time you'll have left over for you.

Create a buffer zone. When looking at how much time you have in a day and what you want to do, create a buffer zone around each activity that allows 10 to 25 percent more time than your estimate. This will accommodate unexpected delays, and you can spend unused buffer time any way you want to!

Consolidate. Plan ways to combine two or three similar tasks. For example, plan to write and send several e-mails when you log on to check received messages instead of logging on and off just to send one message. When you go upstairs or downstairs, take something with you that needs to be put away.

Prioritize your day. What would you like to accomplish today? Which is the most important or difficult task on your list? Make that your first priority. Resist the temptation to do all the little things first "to get them out of the way." Continue prioritizing until you have a number next to each item on your list.

Cut your to-do list in half. Delegate anything that can be delegated and simply cross off those items that have been on your list forever. If these things were really important, you probably would have done them by now. Don't burden yourself with unnecessary tasks.

Keep your list to a minimum. On your daily to-do list, include only those tasks that you reasonably expect you can complete today.

Know When to Quit

Pare down your commitments. Assess your involvement with various committees, boards, groups, and clubs. Is the time you are spending on these commitments aligned with your values? Are you getting a sense of satisfaction or fulfillment from your involvement? Politely excuse yourself from those commitments that are creating any undue stress.

Just say no. Don't let guilt make you take on more than you can handle. According to Miss Manners, the polite way to refuse is to offer an apology but no excuse. She suggests the following three polite denials:

- "Oh, I'm terribly sorry, but I can't."
- "I'd love to, but I'm afraid it's impossible."
- "Unfortunately, I can't, but I hope you can find someone."

Ask for help. If you're doing more than your fair share of work around the house, ask other household members which tasks they would be willing to pick up. You might find that your husband doesn't mind vacuuming or that your teenager likes ironing.

Don't Underestimate the Power of Exercise

By now you know all about the physical benefits of exercise. But did you know that you can also improve your mood through exercise? In a six-week study, 85 women completed mood surveys before and after exercise. Working out put them in better humor, say researchers at Concordia University in Montreal.

At the end of the day, look back on your uncompleted tasks. Why were they left uncompleted? What held you up? How can you make sure they get done the next day?

Shuttle your shuttling responsibilities. A 1999 report by the Washington-based Surface Transportation Policy Project showed that American mothers with kids in school spend an average of 66 minutes each day driving. If it's safe, encourage children who are old enough to walk, bike, or skate to school and to after-school activities — or use public transportation. If other mothers you know are in the same bind, see if you can work out a weekly schedule of pickups and drop-offs that provides all of you with a little extra free time.

Make Time for You

Set limits. Carve out a chunk of time that is your "do not disturb" time. Let everyone in your household know about this time and make it clear that you are to be interrupted only in case of emergency (give them your definition of "emergency," if necessary). Go through possible scenarios with them to make sure they understand. *Hint:* It's a lot easier on everyone if you spend your "do not disturb" time behind a closed door.

ARE YOU GIVING YOURSELF ENOUGH TIME?

Many people (especially optimists!) have trouble managing their time because they underestimate how long activities really take. For example, if you are always late for work, try timing your drive tomorrow. You might find that it's a longer drive than you estimated and that you haven't been allowing yourself enough time to get there. While you're at it, time how long it takes from the moment you wake up to the moment you leave for work. Have you been underestimating there too? Having a more realistic estimate of the time it takes for routine tasks will keep you from running late and will help you be more productive throughout your day. So start timing now!

Designate a night to do your own thing. If your children are old enough to fend for themselves, consider making one night a week a night when they are all on their own. This can be your time to take a class, read, write, draw, or do whatever it is that brings you happiness. A night of alone time is also a good way to help children develop independence.

Get up earlier. If you can't find time for yourself during the day, try getting up before everyone else in your household. The wee hours of the morning are the most peaceful, quiet hours of the day — the ideal time to do something for yourself. Just be sure to go to bed a little earlier to ensure that you get enough sleep.

Schedule in joyful activities. Plan time to do things that give you joy, such as spending time with your children, visiting friends and family, gardening, or whatever. Then schedule everything else around that time. Why should it be the reverse?

> *We always have time enough,*
> *if we will but use it aright.*
>
> — Johann Wolfgang von Goethe

Time is the coin of your life.
It is the only coin you have, and only you
can determine how it will be spent.
Be careful lest you let other people
spend it for you.

— Carl Sandburg

Strike one activity. Eliminate one activity that you do on a regular basis that provides you with little or no satisfaction and only adds to your sense of being overwhelmed.

Turn waiting time into free time. To make more productive use of time spent waiting for someone or something, keep a project box, basket, or bag near your telephone or in your car. Or simply use this time to relax and appreciate your surroundings.

Chapter 7

Simplify Daily Living

In this chapter . . .

- *Seek Simplicity*
- *Celebrate Today*
- *Connect with Nature*
- *Stretch Your Mind*
- *Think Positively*
- *Nourish Your Soul*

I t's not easy to live simply in our complex world. But truly, life is as simple or as complicated as we make it. We can scurry here and there, trying to keep up with the quickening pace around us, or we can slow down and maybe even stop to enjoy the simpler pleasures — most of which can be found in our own homes and backyards.

Seek Simplicity

If you want to live a simpler life, the secret is to string together a series of simpler days, week after week, month after month, year after year. And that means making new choices about how you spend your time and energy — and learning to seek simplicity in all you do.

Shortcuts to a Simpler Life

Try to keep up with things. Keeping up is a lot easier than catching up.

Get into "wash and wear." Go through your clothes closets and drawers and pull out those articles of clothing that require special care, such as dry cleaning or ironing. Consider giving these items away. When you buy new clothes, choose clothes that are machine washable and do not need to be ironed.

Get your hair styled in a way that is natural for it. If you have straight hair, get a good cut that accentuates the straightness. If you have curly hair, wear it curly. Try a new cut or styling product designed for your hair type. Going natural saves time and energy. If you've been thinking about getting a really short haircut, do it. Most short cuts look great with little or no blow-drying or fuss.

Put decisions in perspective. If you have trouble making a decision, ask yourself if it will matter in five years. If it won't, then you can relax in the knowledge that there is more than one "right" decision.

Do a little bit at a time. When you are faced with a task that you do not particularly relish, break it down into smaller tasks. Getting a small amount done in several spurts will make the chore much more pleasant.

Limit the number of choices you have to make on a daily basis. Pare down your wardrobe to your favorite outfits. Plan weekly meals in advance and post the plan on the refrigerator so you don't have to think about what's for dinner when you come home exhausted.

Ask kids to help. Give your children simple things to do that can help keep them (and you) organized. For example, keep a file rack on the kitchen counter or other common area and assign a different color folder to each child into which they are responsible for putting paperwork from school that requires your attention.

Resist the urge to do just one more thing or buy just one more thing.

Celebrate Today

We're always so busy thinking about and planning for the future. But what's the point when you waste the here and now? Don't focus on tomorrow; rejoice in what you have and make the most of *today.*

If It Feels Good, Do It

S-t-r-e-t-c-h. You don't even have to get out of bed to incorporate some stretching into your morning routine! Lie on your back and reach your arms up and over your head. With your toes pointing straight up to the ceiling, push out through your heels and reach your fingertips as far back as you can. Really stretch; hold for five seconds and release. Do it again, but this time stretch only through your right side. Then stretch only through your left side. Stretching gets the blood circulating to your head to give you a rush of energy to start your day.

Center yourself. Take a few moments each morning to think about how you will keep your life in balance today. If you know that you will need to work late, think about how you can squeeze some fun or relaxation into your day.

If you feel like dancing, go ahead and move your feet! If you feel like singing, belt out a tune at the top of your lungs!

Smile! Smiling can't solve all your problems, but the simple act of smiling makes you feel better automatically. Try it. Smile at everyone you pass today and see how it feels. Don't be surprised if people smile back, which will make you feel doubly good.

Explore the ordinary. While walking around your neighborhood, driving to work, or just sitting in your backyard, look more closely at the things around you. Look for something you've never noticed before. There is a simple but profound pleasure in discovery.

If you're feeling unappreciated, appreciate yourself.

Throw a party for no reason at all.

Yak, yak, yak. Social contact with friends may help keep your heart healthy. Think of face-to-face conversation as an alternative form of entertainment to television.

Gain a Fresh Perspective

Focus on what you have, rather than what you have not. Always, there will be people who have more wealth, charm, and abilities than you, just as there will always be people who have far less than you. Be content with what you have today.

Accept that you aren't perfect. It's okay — no one is perfect. People will still love you even when you make mistakes. They may even love you more for it. Accept that others have shortcomings too. Forgiving others' mistakes heals both parties and frees us to learn from the past and move forward.

Make time for family and friends. Studies show that the happiest people are those who feel satisfied with their family life and friendships.

Don't double-book yourself. Sometimes, in our quest to make the most productive use of our time, we make one set of plans for early in the day and another set of plans for later in the day. But this doesn't allow for unexpected delays that might occur, and having to rush to the second activity takes away much of the enjoyment.

Tomorrow is another day. If grief or sorrow, pain or suffering does not allow you to rejoice today, remember that this, too, shall pass. Every once in a while on our journey, we have to go through a dark tunnel. Challenge yourself to keep moving and eventually you will see the light on the other side.

Stick to the truth. Do your best to speak the truth about all things. If you have a tendency to tell little white lies (or big, brazen lies), then you have to remember everything you tell everyone. This not only creates stress but also eats up a lot of energy. Being true to yourself and honest with others will set you free.

> *Finish every day and be done with it.*
> *You have done what you could.*
>
> — Ralph Waldo Emerson

Cultivate close friendships. It is better to have one or two really close friends than a dozen acquaintances. Good friends are those with whom you can talk about nothing and anything. They let you be yourself — and love you anyway. They bring joy and happiness to your life if you let them. Robert Louis Stevenson once wrote, "A friend is a present you give yourself."

Connect with Nature

There's a whole other world out there that is moving at the same pace today as it did thousands of years ago. The sun rises each morning with precision and certainty and sets each evening as it has since the beginning of time. When was the last time you watched the sun set or rise, or took a walk around the block to enjoy the sights and sounds of nature?

Appreciate the Everyday "Wonders"

Tune in to the sounds of nature. There's something reassuring and soothing about nature's rhythms and sounds. The sounds of nature actually help ease stress and may help keep at bay those physical problems with strong links to your emotions, such as heart attack and high blood pressure.

Bring nature inside. If you can't get "back to nature" as often as you'd like, try listening to audiotapes of nature sounds. Get comfortable, close your eyes, and listen to the sounds of woodland birds and crickets or the steady rhythm of ocean waves breaking over rocks.

Do nothing. Schedule some time for doing nothing at all except to sit and daydream and wonder at the universe. You can do it anywhere, but if you walk to a peaceful place in nature, so much the better.

Explore your neighborhood. Go outside and look for things you hadn't noticed before — even in your own backyard. Just take notice of what you see and any thoughts or ideas that pop into your head. Taking a closer look not only encourages curiosity but can also lead to making some amazing connections. And it's fun!

Sit outside at dusk and watch it get dark.

Take nourishment from the sun. Sunlight helps your skin make vitamin D, which, in turn, helps your body absorb calcium and then deposit it in your bones and teeth. Just 10 to 15 minutes of direct sun exposure to your face, arms, and hands three times a week stimulates all the vitamin D your body needs. For more prolonged exposure to sun, be sure to apply sunscreen.

Join a bicycling or hiking club and participate in regular outings.

TRY NATURE JOURNALING

Nature journaling, quite simply, is the act of recording your observations about the natural world at a particular time and place and becoming, in the process, directly involved in that world. Try the following exercise, excerpted from *Keeping a Nature Journal: Discover a Whole New Way of Seeing the World Around You* by Clare Walker Leslie and Charles E. Roth (Storey Books, 2000):

> Go find a piece of paper; it doesn't matter what type or size. Find any pencil, marker, or drawing tool. Now gather up your eyes, take a deep breath, and ask yourself: "What is happening outdoors, this particular season, this time of day, and in this particular place where I live?" (You can be outdoors, or inside looking out.) Draw a cloud, a bird flying by, a tree branch, ivy vines on a building wall, a potted plant, or a garden flower. Don't judge your drawing. You are not an artist yet. You are a scientist, simply recording what you see, in this moment in time. Be very quiet, be very still. Slow your breathing and think only "bud," "plant," "bird." After one minute or less, no more, write what you drew and go on to the next sighting, keeping it relevant to season, time of day, and place.

Stretch Your Mind

Learning contributes to our sense of general well-being, perhaps because it helps us better understand ourselves and our world. When you make it a lifelong pursuit, learning can help simplify your life by opening your eyes to possibilities you never knew existed.

Expand Your Horizons

Read. It's amazing what you can learn by reading — even when you're not actively trying to learn!

Try new things. Push your limits — physically, socially, emotionally, intellectually, and spiritually — and allow yourself the opportunity to discover and appreciate the greatness within you.

Spend free time really getting to know your area. Read up on the history of your village, town, or city. Visit its gardens, parks, recreational areas, and natural resources. What does each one have to offer and what is the best time of year to go there?

Better yourself through learning. Whether you want to advance your career, change careers, or simply better your mind, take deliberate action to continue your education. Set learning goals by following your curiosity.

Expand your universe. Just as a goldfish grows larger in a larger bowl, people grow according to the size of their world — not physically, but mentally. Actively incorporate learning into your daily life by reading, listening, experimenting, observing, and thinking. Just beware: Expanding your mind may transform your life! Here are a few suggestions for expanding your universe:

- Get a library card — and use it.
- Visit museums and historical landmarks.
- Listen to books on tape while doing your housework.
- Attend workshops and seminars.
- Learn how to do something you've always wanted to do.
- Join a book discussion group.
- Try a food you've never tried before.
- Drive a different way home from work.
- See what happens when you do "this" instead of "that."

Share thoughts and ideas. Plan and participate in activities that enable you to meet and spend time with other people who share your values.

Learn on-line. If you have access to the Internet, you have volumes upon volumes of knowledge at your fingertips. Start exploring and see where your explorations lead you. You can even take some college classes on-line.

Get college credit for your life experience. Most colleges recognize the educational value of your experiences, which provides an opportunity for you to get a jump-start on a college degree. You may be able to create a portfolio to document your experiential learning — and earn up to 36 college credits. You also may take what might be considered the final exam in any number of subjects and gain credit that way. Ask at your local college about the College-Level Examination Program (CLEP) tests, the Advanced Placement Program (APP), and the American College Testing Program (ACT-PEP).

Think Positively

When you think positively, it's positively contagious. Change your attitude about one aspect of your life and watch how it automatically improves other areas of your life as well.

It's What You Make of It

Keep your eyes open for all things good. When you look for the best in people, places, and things, that's what you will find.

Think good thoughts. What you choose to think and believe and say right now will shape your future. Upon awakening, while working, and before going to bed, notice what you are thinking. Is it positive or negative?

EXPECTATION OR PREDICTION?

There's a wonderful story in *The Way of the Peaceful Warrior* by Dan Millman that illustrates how our attitudes shape our experiences. It goes something like this:

A wise old man is resting at the side of the road. A traveler approaches and asks him if he knows what the people are like in the town up ahead. The wise old man asks him, "What were the people like in the town you just came from?" to which the traveler replies, "Oh, they were rude and nasty and I couldn't trust anyone." And so the wise old man tells him that the people in the town up ahead are exactly the same. And the traveler trudges off. A little while later, another traveler stops to ask the wise old man if he knows what the people are like up in the town ahead. The wise man responds with the same question he posed to the first traveler, to which the second traveler replies, "Oh, they are the most wonderful and loving and caring people a man could ever hope to know." And so the wise old man tells the traveler that the people in the town up ahead are all that and more.

Find the silver lining. For every action, there is an equal and opposite reaction. Look for the positive in everything negative that happens in your life.

Attitude is everything. Two little boys were playing on the beach at the edge of the ocean when suddenly a large wave rushed over them. When the wave receded, one boy was crying and the other was laughing. They were both hit by the same wave, but each perceived it very differently. Remember that it's not *what* happens to us, but what *attitude* we choose that shapes our experiences.

Keep a "can do" attitude. It will help you make friends and achieve whatever your heart desires.

Accept serendipity. *Webster's* defines *serendipity* as "the finding of valuable or agreeable things not sought for." As you think about what would bring more meaning and satisfaction to your life, pay close attention to what is going on around you. Serendipitous events happen all the time; we just don't always recognize them!

Turn negative energy into positive energy. By taking charge of your thoughts, you can turn them into a powerful source of inner strength and confidence. Let's say, for example, that your best friend becomes upset with you about something you've done. Your initial response is hurt or anger (negative energy) because you think you've done nothing wrong. But then you think about what happened and, in reviewing the situation, you discover something about yourself that you decide to change. In this way, you can be thankful for the experience.

Acknowledge negative thoughts. In her book *Heart Thoughts,* Louise L. Hay says, "You don't have to fight your thoughts when you want to change things. When that negative voice comes up, you can say: 'Thank you for sharing.' You are not giving your power over to the negative thought, and yet you are not denying that it is there. You are saying: 'Okay, you're there and thank you for sharing, and I'm choosing to do something else. I don't want to buy into that anymore, I want to create another way of thinking.' Don't fight your thoughts. Acknowledge them and go beyond them."

Walk tall. Good posture makes you look better and feel better. So stand up straight, lift your chin so that it's parallel to the floor, tuck in your abdomen and buttocks, and relax your shoulders.

Do You Feel Lucky?

Marc Myers, author of *How to Make Luck: Seven Secrets Lucky People Use to Succeed,* believes that if you can change your behavior, you can improve your luck. He says that luck is different from chance. You can't control or predict chance, but you can control your response to what happens to you. He also believes that projecting an image of being lucky attracts luck your way. Here are a few of Myers's suggestions to give yourself a fortunate image and boost your luck:

- Believe that you are lucky and you will act luckier.

- If something bad happens, get over it as quickly as you can.
- Be humble about your good fortune.
- Project confidence without being cocky.
- Think before you act, and if you make a mistake, admit it.
- Be generous without expecting anything in return.

Nourish Your Soul

One way to simplify daily living is to open your heart to your community and to your Higher Power. Find meaningful ways to connect with friends and strangers alike. Establishing a link with yourself and others is like feeding your soul.

Take Action

Be of service. Whether you volunteer for community service projects, help at a school, or visit senior citizens, by giving of your time you help make the world a better place and bring more fulfillment to your own life.

Cultivate close friendships. Spend time with people who support your efforts to live according to your values. Attend services with a community of believers. Look for and attend a Voluntary Simplicity group in your area. Or start your own support group or study circle among friends, neighbors, or coworkers.

Practice random acts of kindness. A good deed or an altruistic act can do wonders for your heart — physically, emotionally, and spiritually. Try these random acts of kindness:

- Brush snow off a stranger's car in a parking lot.
- Send flowers anonymously to someone you know who could use a little cheering up.
- Leave candies on the chairs of coworkers while they are at lunch.
- If someone is waiting to pull out into traffic and it is safe to do, allow that person to go ahead of you.
- Pay the toll for the car behind you at a tollbooth.
- Leave store coupons near the coupon items on supermarket shelves.
- Place a quarter in a gumball machine or coin return of a pay phone.
- Send an anonymous contribution to a favorite charity.

Withhold criticism or judgment. The more you refrain from passing judgment on others, the less you will hear yourself.

Converse with your Higher Power — aloud or in your head. Ask for help during difficult times. Pray for the welfare of a friend or family member. Offer thanks for the beauty and goodness in the world. Verbalize your thoughts and dilemmas.

Give yourself a 15-minute time-out every day. Spend it quietly doing nothing or doing something that brings you joy.

Appreciate your surroundings. Look for beauty in the people, places, and things that you come into contact with each day.

Give a hug, or ask for one.

Make Sunday (or one day a week) a day of rest. Plan to share time with family and friends. Drive up north to your Aunt Martha's. Invite your neighbors for a cookout. Don't feel that you have to do anything special; just be together.

Keep a good-news journal. Take a few minutes at the end of each day to write down the good things that happened throughout your day. On a day when you're feeling down, read through your journal.

Choose to be happy.

Resources

Health & Wellness

Fitness Link
www.fitnesslink.com

This informative on-line resource provides practical, in-depth information about nutrition, exercise, lifestyle changes, mind/body, and fitness programs, with tips for getting started. It also includes the latest fitness news, updated daily.

Health Central
www.healthcentral.com

Established by Dr. Dean Edell, this site is a reliable source of information about a variety of health conditions, indexed A–Z. Click on "Free Personal Health Profile" for a personal health risk assessment. You also can sign up to receive a free weekly e-mail newsletter with news and information personally tailored to your interests.

Mayo Clinic On-Line
www.mayohealth.com

The Mayo Clinic site includes a searchable library, practical advice for first aid, health centers for news and information about treating specific diseases and conditions, quizzes and health assessments, and even a virtual cookbook with a variety of tasty, healthful recipes. Sign up for a free e-mail bulletin with weekly updates.

Money & Finances

Bankrate.com
www.bankrate.com
Bankrate.com provides objective financial data and research and editorial information to help consumers make informed decisions about mortgages, credit cards, new and used auto loans, money market accounts and CDs, checking and ATM fees, home equity lines and loans, and online banking fees.

Consumer Credit Counseling Service
(800) 388-2227 (national office)
A nonprofit community organization, CCCS provides free, confidential financial counseling on budgeting and credit management. Its debt repayment plan is a legal alternative to bankruptcy that allows financially stressed consumers to repay creditors over time. Check the Yellow Pages of your local telephone directory or call toll-free information to find an office near you.

Dollar Stretcher Club
The Dollar Stretcher
P.O. Box 23785
Fort Lauderdale, FL 33307
(954) 772-1696
www.stretcher.com
The Dollar Stretcher offers a virtual meeting place for people who are helping each other to gain control of their finances through frugal living. For a schedule of meetings, go to www.stretcher.com

and click on "Dollar Stretcher Club." You can also get current and past issues of a weekly newsletter called *Living Better . . . For Less.* Or send $2 to the address above for a sample issue.

Simple Living

Balancing Act
P.O. Box 309
Ghent, NY 12075-0309
http://members.aol.com/balancinga/ba.html
Balancing Act is a bimonthly newsletter that helps people save money and simplify their lives. For a sample issue, send $1 plus a SASE to the above address or visit the Web page. To subscribe for a year, send $6 along with your name and address.

Life On Purpose Institute
P.O. Box 834
Flat Rock, NC 28731-0834
(800) 668-0183
(828) 697-9239
www.lifeonpurpose.com
The Life On Purpose Institute is dedicated to purposeful service, mindful and abundant simplicity, and spiritual serenity. Its Web site features inspiring stories about people who are living purposeful lives. The site offers a self-test to help you determine if you are living life on purpose. It also offers a free subscription to *Purposeful Pondering* e-zine and a free five-part virtual seminar that will arrive in your e-mail over a week's time.

The Simple Living Network
P.O. Box 233
Trout Lake, WA 98650
(800) 318-5725
www.simpleliving.net
The Simple Living Network is an on-line service with thousands of pages of information, tools, and resources for people who want to live a simpler, healthier, more environmentally conscious lifestyle. The Web site features a free weekly e-zine.

Simple Times
simple-times-subscribe@egroups.com
A free e-mail newsletter for simple, frugal living from the author of *Frozen Assets: How to Cook for a Day and Eat for a Month*. Regular topics include frugality, using leftovers, freezer meals, shopping tips, food prep and storage, and more. To subscribe to this biweekly e-mail newsletter, send a blank e-mail message to the above address.

> *Happiness comes from the capacity to feel deeply, to enjoy simply, to think freely, to be needed.*
>
> — Storm Jameson

Index

Page numbers in **boldface** refer to charts.